MAD

The BEST of the WORST!

D1533147

by
"The Usual Gang of Idiots"

edited by John Ficarra

designed by Patricia Dwyer

CONTENTS

MAD Magazine

EDITOR John Ficarra
ART DIRECTOR Sam Viviano
SENIOR EDITORS Charlie Kadau, Joe Raiola
ASSOCIATE EDITORS Dave Croatto, Jacob Lambert
ASSISTANT ART DIRECTOR Ryan Flanders
PRODUCTION ARTIST Doug Thomson

FRONT COVER ARTIST Mark Fredrickson

SPECIAL MAD THANKS
Pete Croatto, Joe Daley, Doug Gilford, Peter Harper,
Bartek Jalonek, Max Korn, Sandy Resnick, Bill Shapiro

SPECIAL THANKS
Christine Austin, Jeremy Biloon, Jim Childs, Rose Cirrincione,
Lauren Hall Clark, Jacqueline Fitzgerald, Christine Font, Jenna
Goldberg, Hillary Hirsch, Suzanne Janso, David Kahn, Mona Li,
Amy Mangus, Robert Marasco, Kimberly Marshall, Amy Migliaccio,
Nina Mistry, Dave Rozzelle, Adriana Tierno, Vanessa Wu

Who Is Alfred E. Neuman?

By Frank Jacobs

One day in the 1960s a letter was delivered to the MAD offices bearing no name or address. Other than a postage stamp, the envelope bore only a picture of the magazine's cover boy, Alfred E. Neuman.

Clearly, the gap-toothed face of the idiot kid had become iconic. Alfred and MAD, to use an overworked phrase, were joined at the hip. Already the grinning face had shown up in unlikely places: placards of him as a candidate — "You could do worse, you always have!" — were flaunted at political conventions. His features were sculpted in ice at a Dartmouth Winter Carnival. Fred Astaire danced in an Alfred mask during a TV special. A party of climbers planted a Neuman flag atop Mount Everest.

Alfred owes his place in history to four men. The first was MAD's first editor, Harvey Kurtzman, who glimpsed the grinning face, captioned "Me worry?" on a postcard in 1954.

"It was a kid that didn't have a care in the world, except mischief," Kurtzman recalled. The boy soon made his way into the pages of the magazine, though he was as yet unnamed.

Kurtzman had been using the Neuman name mostly because it had the ring of a nonentity — although there was a Hollywood composer named Alfred Newman. Misspelled, with the added "E," it too was integrated into the magazine.

When Al Feldstein replaced Kurtzman as editor, he decided to link "Alfred E. Neuman" with the face of the idiot kid. The idiot kid made his official debut in 1956 as a write-in candidate for President on the cover of MAD #30, and the magazine now had an official mascot and cover boy. In the next issue, Alfred made his second cover appearance pictured as an addition to Mount Rushmore.

Norman Mingo's classic Alfred.

ME WORRY?

1954 postcard of the "idiot kid."

Though others had their doubts, Nick Meglin, then an assistant editor, believed that MAD should continue to use Alfred as the magazine's cover boy. "You'll have to convince me," said publisher Bill Gaines, who had veto power over all MAD covers. Playing up to Gaines' interest in archaeology, Meglin submitted a rough sketch of Alfred in an Egyptian tomb (MAD #31) and one or two others that emerged as cover illustrations later. Having been convinced there were endless possibilities, Gaines agreed that Alfred should reign as the magazine's icon.

And so he has — in a fireworks display (#34), as a guru (#121), a Neumanized George Washington (#181), a

3

California Raisin (#281), a self-reproducing Xerox machine (#356). And posters — Alfred the Hun, Toulouse Neuman, Alfred von Richtofen, the Red Baron. Movie stardom was slow in coming. Alfred's first gig as an "actor" arrived on the cover of #86 as Lawrence of Arabia. He had to wait more than three years for his role as Robin to Adam West's Batman (#105), then two years more when he appeared with Bonnie and Clyde (#119). From then on, Alfred's show-biz career skyrocketed, especially when billboarding MAD's spoofs of the Star Trek and Star Wars films.

The Neuman face was created by Norman Mingo. Curiously, none of MAD's artists, though extremely versatile, has been able to render accurately the Mingo prototype. When Mingo died in 1980, his obituary in The New York Times identified him in its headline as the "Illustrator Behind 'Alfred E. Neuman' Face."

Several decades ago, Charles Winick, a psychologist, polled some 400 readers of MAD. He found that Alfred was liked especially by low achievers. "Less successful students," Winick observed, "are more likely to identify with Neuman because he conveys a feeling of failure, defeat, defensiveness, and uninvolvement. His non-worry slogan has a 'let the world collapse, I don't care' quality, and his appearance suggests stupidity."

Today, Winick might well change his views were he to examine many of the postings on the Internet. But he was right on one score: Alfred does suggest stupidity, which may lead to ill feeling on the part of a lad who is told he resembles MAD's mascot. Such a reaction occurred in 1958, the slighted youth apparently being Britain's Prince Charles. A photograph of the bonnie young heir to the throne, who was then nine years old, had been carried in newspapers throughout the United States. Prince Charles was smiling in the photograph, and his face, so thought many MAD readers who subsequently wrote in, bore a striking resemblance to Alfred E. Neuman.

MAD published several of the comments, along with the photo, on its letters page. A few weeks later arrived the following letter, postmarked London:

Dear Sirs,
No it isn't a bit — not the least little bit like me.
So jolly well stow it! See! Charles P.

Did the letter really come from Prince Charles? Art director John Putnam, who knew about such things, analyzed it. The handwriting was typical of a well-educated nine-year-old. The stationery was triple cream-laid paper, bearing the copper-engraved crest of the Duke of Edinburgh, and would have been commercially impossible to duplicate. The signature, "Charles P.," was eminently correct, the P standing for Princeps, which is how Charles would have likely signed his name. A contact at the British Embassy in New York City noted that the postmark revealed that the letter had been mailed within "a very short walking distance of Buckingham Palace."

Putnam weighed the evidence and pronounced that barring someone having pilfered the royal family's stationery, the letter was authentic.

What is the source of the "What — Me Worry?" Boy? MAD asked its readers to help out and was deluged by suggestions and theories. The kid was used in 1915 to advertise a patent medicine; he was a newspaperman named Old Jack; he was taken from a biology textbook as an example of a person who lacked iodine; he was a testimonial on advertisements for painless dentistry; he was originated by comedian Garry Moore; he was a greeting-card alcoholic named Hooey McManus; he was a Siamese boy named Watmi Worri. One reader dug up a 1909 German calendar bearing a version of the inane smiling face.

By far the most pertinent correspondence came from a lawyer representing a Vermont woman named Helen Pratt Stuff. She claimed that her late husband, Harry Stuff, had created the kid in 1914, naming him "The Eternal Optimist." Stuff's copyrighted drawing, she charged, was the

I consider Mr. Neuman to be our trademark at this point.

Dear Sirs
No it isn't a bit — not the least little bit like me. So jolly well stow it! See! Charles. P.

BUCKINGHAM PALACE

"The Original Optimist"

4

urce of Alfred E. Neuman and she was taking MAD to court prove it.

Thus began the great Alfred E. Neuman lawsuit. The akes were not small. If MAD lost, it would be liable for llions of dollars in damages. And Alfred no longer would permitted to show his worriless countenance in any AD publication or property.

MAD's attorney, Martin Scheiman, hired tracers on both asts to hunt for pictures of the idiot kid that had been blished before 1914. A number of renderings popped up, veral of them almost dead ringers for Harry Stuff's "Original otimist." It became evident that portraits had been ating around the United States since fore the turn of the century. But act dates were hard to put down.

Mrs. Stuff had sued before and d won several cases. Scheiman gued that Stuff, in copyrighting s "Original Optimist," had not eated an original face — that e had based his version of e idiot kid on pictures in e public domain. In other rds, Stuff's illustration as not copyrightable. lso, there was no pyright notice on ost copies of Stuff's awings, making it npossible for MAD to how it was copyrighted.

The trial of the case in nited States District Court as full of legal infighting, most of hich would bore readers of this book tears. Nevertheless, Neumanphiles uld rejoice at the deference shown eir idol. Alfred, for years the butt f a thousand jokes, was, for nce, being treated

with respect. For example, this exchange between Mrs. Stuff's attorney, Samuel J. Stoll, and Gaines:

STOLL: Has any MAD issue appeared since the adoption of this character, Alfred Neuman, without Mr. Neuman appearing on one of its pages or cover page?

GAINES: I do not believe that any issue has come out without featuring him in some way, sometimes more prominently than others, but he would always be there.

STOLL: Would you consider Mr. Neuman to be a rather prominent and substantial part of your publication?

GAINES: I consider Mr. Neuman to be our trademark at this point, an identification with the magazine and, as such, very helpful.

After listening to some six thousand words of arguments and testimony, and poring over several hundred pictures of Alfred and his ancestors, Judge Lloyd F. MacMahon arrived at his decision. MAD, he opined, had not infringed on the Stuff copyright, mainly because the copyright notice was rarely included on copies of Stuff's picture. To put it another way, it was as if the grinning boy was a bastard orphan and that MAD had every legal right to adopt him, give him loving care, and provide him with a Christian name.

What — him worry? No longer. The idiot kid was, at last, legitimate.

Alfred as rendered by MAD's current cover artist, Mark Fredrickson.

Yoga is great practice for marriage — all you do i
bend over backwards when someone tells you to
—Alfred E. Neuma

"Look, Mom—no more cavities!"

Crust Gumpaste helps gums take the place of teeth by coating them with a hard white enamel finish! Just the thing for punks who get their teeth knocked out from running around with teen-age gangs.

Fluidsteel is a trademark for Proctor & Rumble's exclusive liquid metal gum-center.
© 1958, The Proctor & Rumble Co.

Artist: Kelly Freas

#43 DEC '58

#27 APR '56

"VISITING THE GRANDPARENTS" by William Elder. Number 1 in the series "Of Hom

While you are visiting—

What makes a glass of beer taste so good?

Malted barley—with important body minerals plus liquid matter. For thing that makes glass of beer taste so good is terrible thirst.

Tangy hops. Yes—visiting can be a series of tangy hops if you play your cards right. And you'd be surprised how good free beer tastes!

The way it "goes with everything"—makes beer this country's Beverage of Moderation—the way it fits into our friendly way of life—the way each glass makes us friendlier and friendlier and friendlier.

Artist: Will Elder   Writer: Harvey Kurtzman

Beer Belongs—Enjo

6

Scenes We'd Like to See

Driving The Golden Spike

ART—GEORGE WOODBRIDGE   STORY BY EUGENE ST. JEAN

#48 JUL '59

#51 DEC '59

HUBERT THUMB

Artist: Kelly Freas

PRESENTING THE BILL—reproduced here, is one of a series of original oil paintings, "Practicing Medicine For Fun and Profit", commissioned by Park-David.

Great Moments in Medicine

Once the crisis has passed . . . once the patient has regained his strength . . . once the family is relieved and grateful . . . that's the time when the physician experiences one of the great moments in medicine. In fact, the *greatest moment* in medicine! Mainly, the moment when he presents his bill! That's the time when all of the years of training and study and work seem worthwhile. And there's always the chance that the shock might mean more business for him!

Park-David scientists are proud of their place in the history of practicing medicine for fun and profit, helping to provide doctors with the materials that mean higher fees and bigger incomes. For example, our latest development . . . tranquilizer-impregnated bill paper . . . designed to eliminate the shock and hysteria that comes when the patient gets a look at your bill. Not only will he remain calm when he sees what you've charged . . . now he won't even *care!*

COPYRIGHT 1959—PARK-DAVID & COMPANY, WITH THE BLESSINGS OF THE AMA

PARK-DAVID   *. . . Pioneers in bigger medical bills*

Remember the good old days when people just stole your cash, and not your identity?

—Alfred E. Neuman

Here we go with the 2nd of a three-part series on "Parties." Last issue we looked at "Adult Parties." Next issue we will cover "Kids' Parties." But this time, it's—

THE LIGHTER SIDE OF TEEN

Oh, Daddy! Can I throw a party for the gang?

How do you like that?! My daughter is growing up! She's thirteen, and wants to throw her own shindig! It reminds me of when I was thirteen . . .

. . . and I went to Adrian Burner's party! Boy, that was fun! She and I ended up in the backyard . . . **HEY, WAIT A MINUTE!!**

CERTAINLY NOT!!

Are you **working?** How much do you **make** a week?

What does your **father** do?

I—er—

What do you plan on **becoming**—a doctor, a lawyer, an engineer, **what?**

Well—I—er—

Does your family intend setting you up in **business?**

Can you **support** a family?

Has there ever been any **insanity** in your family?

Gee—I—uh—

  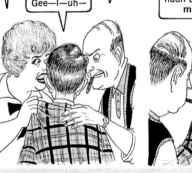

Honest, folks, I just happened to be the fir* **guest** to show up at yo daughter's **party!** I rea hadn't **planned** on gett* **married** tonight!

Hey, **quiet** everybody! Quick! Turn out the **lights!** Here come those **Mepham High Boys**, looking to crash this party!

Oh-oh! They're stopping!

I can't understand how they **always know** exactly where there's a **party** to crash!

MEPHAM HIGH CRASHERS
THIS IS THE PLACE
PARTY!
FUN! FUN!
20 DOLL GIRLS COUNT 'EM 20
ASK FOR MARTHA SUE BOBBI GAY LAURIE PAM RUTH
GET RID OF FRANK, ANDY, STEVE, NORMAN
30 CLOD BOYS FORGET 'EM! 30

8

AGE PARTIES

ARTIST & WRITER: DAVE BERG

Are you plagued by clods who ask stupid questions? We mean the kind of questions to which the answers are painfully obvious. Doesn't it drive you nuts to have to give such answers? Don't you wish you could come up with snappy answers that would put these dolts down, like the cor on TV always do? Well, you can! All you need is a se of humor, a little practice, and a mean, rotten disp tion. You also need to convince yourself that there

MAD'S SNAPPY ANSWERS

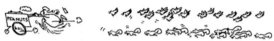

...ing worse than stupid clods who ask pointless unneces- ...questions. Is that clear? Do you undertand what we ...n? Are we getting the point of this article across to ...? Isn't this the perfect time to come up with one of them snappy answers? Okay! Study the typical situations on these pages and practice giving the snappy answers we've printed. Then start making up your own. Before long you'll see how gratifying it is to humiliate people with . . . .

O STUPID QUESTIONS

ARTIST & WRITER: AL JAFFEE

Make Beautiful Hair

B L E C C H

THERE ARE THREE BLECCH SHAMPOOS FOR THREE DIFFERENT HAIR CONDITIONS

Are you a teenage boy with Beautiful Hair? Well no wonder the girls hardly notice you. Today, you've got to be a teenage boy with Blecch hair. Then the girls will scream with delight, roll on the floor and kick their feet when they see you. So why waste another minute? Shampoo your hair with Blecch tonight. Blecch comes in three special formulas:

● For dry hair—a special formula that takes neat crew-cut type hair and lays it down over your ears. ● For oily hair —loosens up that slick-combing stuff so it spills down over your eyes. ● For normal hair—gives it proper body so it mushrooms all over your head. Get the shampoo that's right for you, and make your hair "Blecch"! Yeah! Yeah! Yeah!

SELF-PORTRAIT

WRITER & ARTIST: AL JAFFEE

IN THE DELICATESSEN

ARTIST: DON MARTIN

MAD's Great Moments In Politics

#116 JAN '68

We can fix America's plummeting test scores in math if we all just give 110 percent!

—Alfred E. Neuman

#106 OCT '66

Early One Morning In The Jungle

ARTIST: FRANK FRAZETTA   WRITER: DON EDWING

THERE'S A SOCCER BORN EVERY MINUTE DEPT.

For years, the nation's educators have been howling about the evils inherent in such big time college sports as football and basketball. They contend that there's too much professionalism, that not enough boys have a chance to participate, etc. But no one really lifted a finger to correct the situation until MAD's Athletic Council went to work—and he's come up with a brand new sport that promises to provide good, clean amateur fun for all. Here, then, are the rules for this great new national pastime of the future. Digest them carefully and be the last person in your neighborhood to play . . . as . . .

MAD MAGAZINE
introduces
43-MAN SQUAMISH

ARTIST: GEORGE WOODBRIDGE   WRITER: TOM KOCH

A Squamish team consists of 43 players: the left & right Inside Grouches, the left & right Outside Grouches, four Deep Brooders, four Shallow Brooders, five Wicket Men, three Offensive Niblings, four Quarter-Frummerts, two Half-Frummerts, one Full-Frummert, two Overblats, two Underblats, nine Back-Up Finks, two Leapers and a Dummy.

Each player is equipped with a long hooked stick known as a Frullip. The Frullip is used to halt opposing players attempting to cross your goal line with the Pritz (ball). The Official Pritz is 3¾ inches in diameter and is made of untreated Ibex hide stuffed with Blue Jay feathers.

Play begins with the Probate Judge flipping a new Spanish peseta. If the Visiting Captain calls the toss correctly, the game is immediately cancelled. If he fails to call it correctly, then the Home Team Captain is given his choice of either carrying the Pritz . . . or defending against it.

The game of Squamish is played on a 5-sided field known as a Flutney. The two teams line up at opposite sides of the Flutney and play seven Ogres of fifteen minutes each — unless it rains, in which case they play eight Ogres.

The defending right Outside Grouch signifies that he ready to hurl the Pritz by shouting, "Mi Tio es inferm pero la carretera es verde!"—a wise old Chilean prove that means, "My Uncle is sick, but the highway is gree

The offensive team, upon receiving the Pritz, has five Snivels in which to advance to the enemy goal. If they do it on the ground, it's a Woomik and counts 17 points. If they hit it across with their Frullips, it's a Durmish which only counts 11 points. Only the offensive Niblings and Overblats are allowed to score in the first 6 Ogres.

Special rules, applicable only during the seventh Og turn the game into something very akin to Buck Euch During this final Ogre (and the eighth, if it rains), four Quarter-Frummerts are permitted to either kick throw the Pritz, and the nine Finks are allowed to hec the opposition by doing imitations of Barry Goldwa

A typical seventh Ogre play is shown below. Team "A"— trailing 516—209, is in possession of the Pritz with fourth Snivel and half the Flutney to go. Suddenly, the left Underblat, going for the big one, sends two Shallow Brooders and the Full-Frummert downfield. Obviously, he is going to try for a Woomik when the opposition expects a Durmish. A daring play of this type invariably brings the crowd rising to its feet and heading for the exits.

A variety of penalties keep play from getting out of ha Walling the Pritz, Frullip-gouging, icing on fifth Sniv running with the mob and raunching are all minor infra tions subject to a ten-yard penalty. Major infractio (sending the Dummy home early, interfering with Wick Men, rushing the season, bowing to the inevitable a inability to face facts) are punishable by loss of h the Flutney, except when the Yellow Caution Flag is o

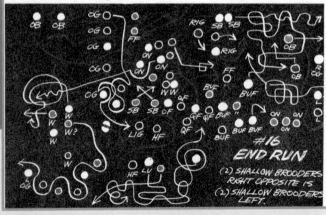

Squamish rules provide for 4 officials: a Probate Judge, a Field Representative, a Head Cockswain and a Baggage Smasher. None has any authority after play has begun. In the event of a disagreement between the officials, a final decision is left up to the spectator who left his car in the parking lot with the lights on and the motor running.

In the event of a tie score, the teams play a sudden-death overtime. The exception to this rule occurs when opposing Left Overblats are both out of the game on personal fouls. When such is the case, the two teams line up on opposite sides of the Flutney and settle the tie by shouting dirty limericks at each other until one team breaks up laughing.

Amateur Squamish players are strictly forbidden to accept subsidies, endorse products, make collect phone calls or eat garlic. Otherwise, they lose their amateur standing. A player may turn Pro, however, merely by throwing a game.

Schools with small enrollments which preclude participation in 43-Man Squamish may play a simplified version of the game: 2-Man Squamish. The rules are identical, except that in 2-Man Squamish, the object of the game is to lose.

The original charter calls for an annual meeting of the National Squamish Rules Committee. At its inaugural meeting, the committee approved a re-wording of Article XVI, Paragraph 77, Section J of the rules. This section, which formerly read: "The offensive left Underblat, in all even-numbered Ogres, must touch down his Frullip at the edge of the Flutney and signal to the Head Cockswain that he is ready for play to continue," has now been simplified

to read: "The offensive left Underblat, in all even-numbered ogres, must touch down his Frullip at the edge of the Flutney and signal to either the Head Cockswain, or to any other official to whom the Head Cockswain may have delegated this authority in writing and in the presence of two witnesses, both of whom shall have been approved and found to be of high moral character by the Office of the Commissioner, that he is ready for play to continue."

"THESE ARE THE VOYAGES OF THE STAR-SHIP 'BOOBY-PRIZE'! ITS MISSION, TO EXPLORE STRA

STAR BLECCH

ARTIST: MORT DRUCKER   WRITER: DICK DE BARTOLO

...V WORLDS, TO SEEK OUT NEW LIFE, AND TO BOLDLY GO WHERE NO MAN HAS EVER GONE BEFORE!"

...is the tar Ship oby-Prize" ... calling ma IV . . .

This is Rama IV! We need help **immediately!** We're suffering from **landslides, earthquakes, poisoned air,** and . . .

I'm not sure if I'm talking to **Rama IV** or **The Los Angeles Chamber of Commerce!**

We'd better beam down and have a look! If you're coming **with** me, Mr. Spook, you'd better step into this "Descanner"!

Sir, I—

You're not turning **chicken,** are you, Mr. Spook?

No, sir— but you're standing in the **Phone Booth!!** **THAT's** the "Descanner"!

Er . . . yes! **I know!** I was just going to **phone ahead!** You know how awkward it could be—dropping in on a planet **unexpectedly!**

...IPP!

ZAP ZAPP!

Remind me to check your **Reassembling Unit!** I think it needs a minor adjustment!

Here—let me help you pull yourself together!

Better **hurry**— because I've got the strangest feeling that my **face** wants to **sit down!**

#115 DEC '67

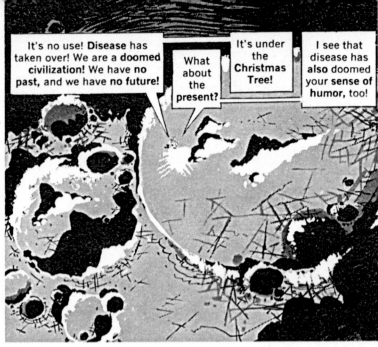

WHAT INDUSTRY CONTRIBUTES MORE TO AIR POLLUTION THAN ANY OTHER?

ARTIST & WRITER:
AL JAFFEE

A ▶

HERE WE GO WITH ANOTHER RIDICULOUS
MAD FOLD-IN

More and more concern is being expressed over the problem of Air Pollution. And yet, year after year, one industry consistently pollutes the air while the vast majority of Americans quietly accept it. To find out who this villain is, fold page in as shown.

FOLD THIS SECTION OVER LEFT

FOLD PAGE OVER LIKE THIS!

◀B FOLD BACK SO "A" MEETS "B"

#127 JUN '69

23

Much has been written about hallucinogenic drugs like LSD, and the glories (or danger
of taking psychedelic "trips". Some unsavory magazines have even featured this topic
their covers in order to sell copies. (See MAD #116.) And so, because MAD is intereste

A PSYCHED

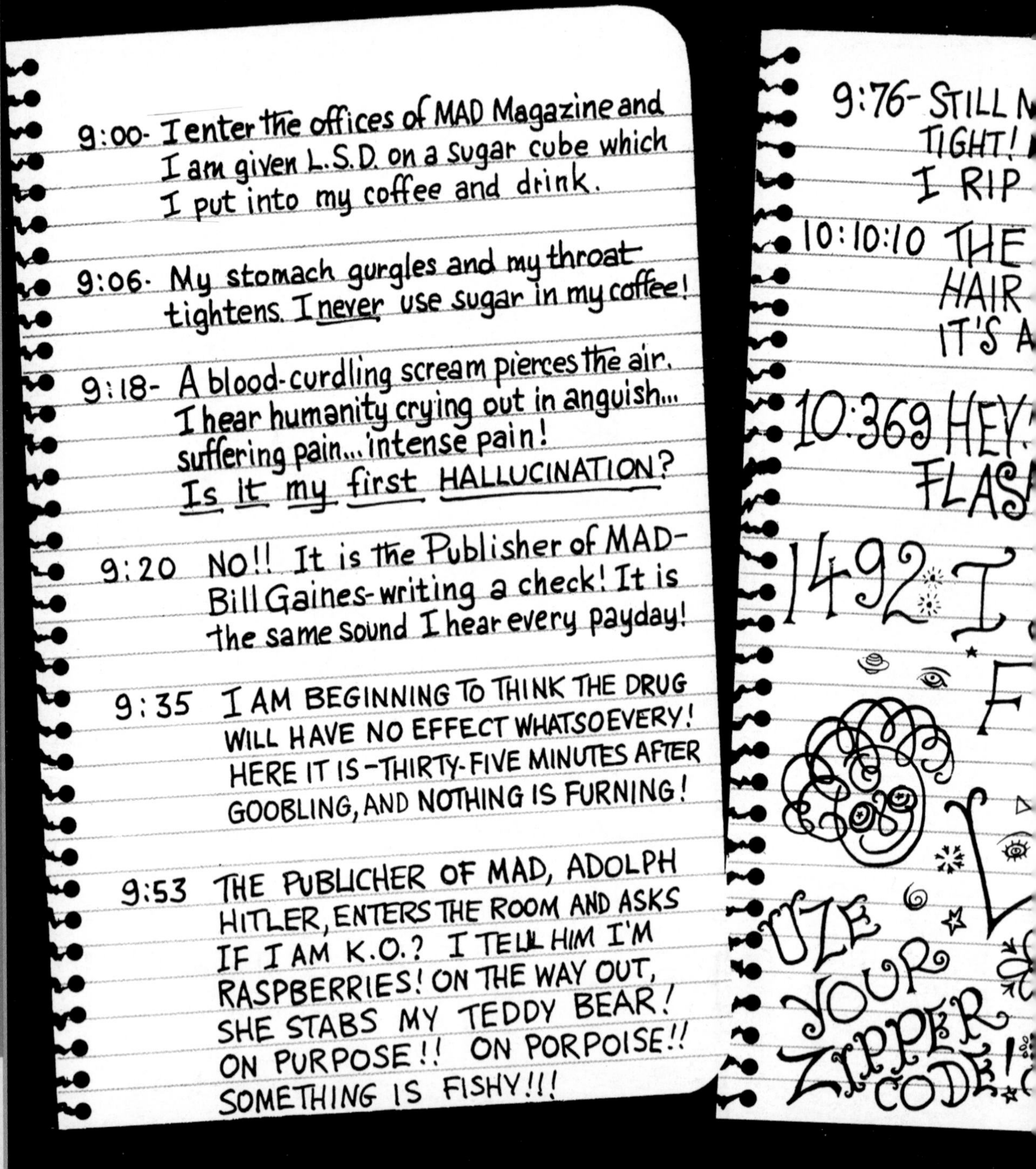

9:00- I enter the offices of MAD Magazine and I am given L.S.D. on a sugar cube which I put into my coffee and drink.

9:06- My stomach gurgles and my throat tightens. I never use sugar in my coffee!

9:18- A blood-curdling scream pierces the air. I hear humanity crying out in anguish... suffering pain... intense pain! Is it my first HALLUCINATION?

9:20 NO!! It is the Publisher of MAD- Bill Gaines-writing a check! It is the same sound I hear every payday!

9:35 I AM BEGINNING TO THINK THE DRUG WILL HAVE NO EFFECT WHATSOEVERY! HERE IT IS—THIRTY-FIVE MINUTES AFTER GOOBLING, AND NOTHING IS FURNING!

9:53 THE PUBLICHER OF MAD, ADOLPH HITLER, ENTERS THE ROOM AND ASKS IF I AM K.O.? I TELL HIM I'M RASPBERRIES! ON THE WAY OUT, SHE STABS MY TEDDY BEAR! ON PURPOSE!! ON PORPOISE!! SOMETHING IS FISHY!!!

9:76- STILL M TIGHT! I RIP

10:10:10 THE HAIR IT'S A

10:369 HEY FLAS

1492 I

F

UZE YOUR ZIPPER CODE!

n truth, because MAD desired to find out once and for all what taking an LSD "trip" was
ke, and mainly because MAD wanted to feature this topic once again in order to sell
opies, we talked one of our writers into taking LSD, and describing his experiences in

ELIC DIARY

WRITER: DICK DEBARTOLO

K! MY SKIN IS ON TOO
TAILOR! LOUSY BURTON!
'THING OFF!!

OISE IS RACING THE
2 MY ARMS!
MS RACE!!!

'OFF THOSE
BRIGHT LICE!!

L FEEL
E ☆

RB YOUR
CAR

12:30 THE PLUBISHER OF MUD, HUGH HEFFER, TAPS ME ON THE BROCCOLI—

90:76 I MAKE OUT SHAPES IN THE ROOM A DESK- A LAMP- A STAGECOACH- A PHUNG

1:15 - PEOPLE ARE STAIRING AT ME! I'M A STAIR-CASE! I TRY TO EXPLAIN THAT SOME FUNNY THINGS HAVE HAPPENED TO MY. BUT IT'S NO.

1:30 - EVERYTHING IS BECOMING EXTREMELY CLEAR! BUT IS IT REALITY? DO I REALLY LIVE? OR DO I JUST EXIST IN A CHINGE OF MY BLUK?

1:45 - WHAT IS NOT? AND WHY, IF WE, DO WE? OF COURSE!

2:00 A blood-curdling scream pierces the air. I hear humanity crying out in anguish... suffering pain... intense pain! IS IT AN HALLUCINATION AT LAST??

2:03 NO!! It is the Publisher of MAD— Bill Gaines- writing another check!

2:05- Everything is back to norbal.

ONE DAY IN A CRASH-PAD

Hey, Man—got anything to eat up here?

Just leftovers, Baby!

ARTIST: DON MARTIN

What kind of leftovers, Man?

Egg yolks, beef gravy with rice, and watermelon juice!

Sounds groovie! I'll have some . . .

SHKLURCH

#139 DEC '70

#137 SEP '70

Introducing A New MAD Feature Which Takes A Humorous Look At The War Between

HAWKS & DOVES

MAJOR HAWKS

PRIVATE DOVES

OFFICERS BEACH CLUB

MAJ. HAWKS

ARTIST & WRITER: AL JAFFEE

LOCKERS

Ever since Television began, situation comedies have been, more or less, the same. Now, all of a sudden, a new situation comedy has come along . . . and it's entirely different from the old-fashioned family fare. It doesn't deal with the same old stupid subjects involving idiotic, unbelievable characters. Instead, it concerns itself with relevant "now" subjects, involving even more idiotic unbelievable characters! Here, then, is MAD's version of . . .

GALL IN THE FAMILY FARE

This Week's Episode: "A Visit From A World War II Buddy"

there—and welcome to the dle American home of TV's and foremost foul-mouthed er-image, Starchie Bunker- . . . and me, his incredibly tupid wife, Meathead . . .

Each week we bring you **another episode** in our lives . . . filled with **hilarious controversy** and uproarious vulgarity! Oh—our "**Special Guest Shock-Word**" for this week is "**FAGGOT**" . . .

And now, before Starchie arrives home from work and starts his usual **tirades** against everyone . . . regardless of **race, creed or national origin** . . . let me tell you a little about **myself!** I was born of **Spanish** parents, and I . . .

Hey, you **dumb Spick!** Di'n't you hear me ringin' the **doorbell?**

And here he is now, folks! AMERICA'S BELOVED BIGOT . . .

ARTIST: ANGELO TORRES   WRITER: LARRY SIEGEL

What a day!! I punched a **Dago**, I belted a **Coon**, and I kicked a **Mick!**

See, Starch? It all evens up! Yesterday you complained you had a **BAD** day!

I'll get the phone . . .

RRRING

Listen to me, you dirty rotten **Hebe!** I **had** it with you pushy **Jews!** When you seen **one Kike**, you seen 'em all!

Starchie, **who's** that on the phone?

My **FATHER!** Boy, I hate all kinds of Jews! Orthodox . . . Reformed . . .

But, **Starchie** . . . Your Father is **Protestant!**

They're the **worst kind!!**

#147 DEC '71

f course you do! Most Americans agree with me! hey ain't laughin' T me . . . they're laughin' WITH me! That's why this show is such a "Hit"!

I'm so popular, I may run for President! Or better still . . . VICE-PRESIDENT!!

There's the doorbell, Starchie! I'll get it!

BRRDING

Starchy, it's your old War buddy!

My buddy! My old World War II buddy! It's gonna be great seein' him again . . . the only man who ever really understood me . . .

Dolf, baby! Where the hell have you been all these years?

I've been alive und vell und liffing in Argentina! You know! Chust like ze old choke . . . heh-heh!

Speaking of old jokes, I'd like you to meet my wife Meathead!

Starchie! THAT man is your old buddy?! Do you know who he is? Do you know what he's done? Do you know what kind of reputation he has? How could you ever have associated with him . . .?!

Aw, he ain't a bad guy— for a Pinko!

There's the doorbell again! I'll get it . . .

RIINNG

Starchie, these two men want to see your buddy . . .

Oh-oh! Ze jig iss up! After all zese years, I knew zey would finally get me! Vell, mein olt buddy, I guess zis iss it!

Chentlemen, under ze Articles uff Var, I am only required to gif you mein name . . . Adolph Hitler . . . mein rank . . . Professional Mischief-Maker . . . und mein serial number, vich is "Vun"! I am now ready to face the War Crimes Commission . . .

We're not from the War Crimes Commission, Dolf, baby! We're from the TV Network! We're here to offer you your own weekly TV series!

First, we'll get you an adorable TV family . . .

Yeah . . . like a dumb wife, two moronic children, and a pet wolf . . .!

If a show with THIS hero is a hit, yours'll be a SMASH!

I've got a great title! "Love—Gestapo Style"!

How about "My Three Storm Troopers"?

Hold it! Listen to this one . . .

Whadya say, Dolf?

No, wait! I've got a better one! "Hunsmoke"!

Wait! I've got it! "Nazi And The Professor"!

No, no, listen to MINE first!

Today . . . television! Tomorrow . . . Ze WORLD!!

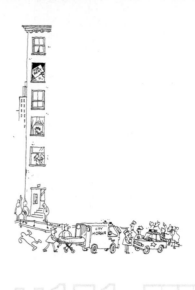

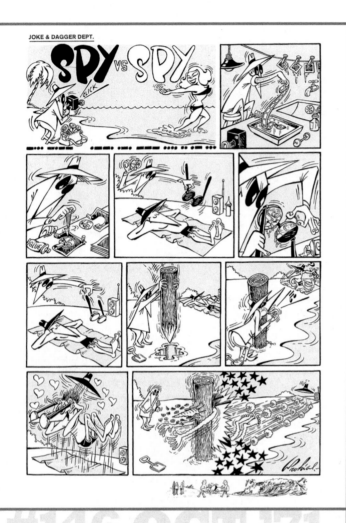

#146 OCT '71

Experience is what makes you pause
briefly before going ahead and making
the same mistake.

—Alfred E. Neuman

#151 JUN '72

BACK IN THE OPERATING ROOM WITH DON MARTIN
DURING A HEART TRANSPLANT

32

A MOVING JUNGLE TALE

WRITER: DON EDWING   ARTIST: JACK DAVIS

All lawyers are cut from the same cloth — fleece.

—Alfred E. Neuman

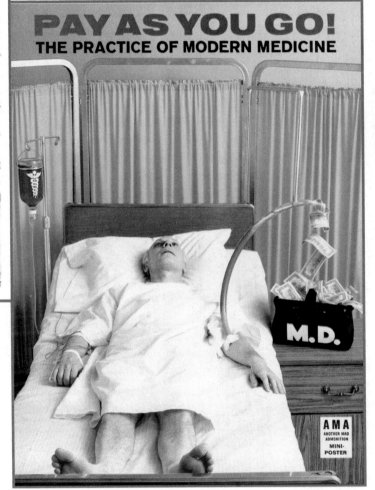

PAY AS YOU GO!
THE PRACTICE OF MODERN MEDICINE

M.D.

A M A
ANOTHER MAD
ADMONITION
MINI-POSTER

Who Knows What Evils Lurk In

THE SHADOW

he Hearts Of Men?
KNOWS

WRITER & ARTIST: SERGIO ARAGONES

Scenes We'd Like To See

ARTIST: JACK RICKARD   WRITER: DON EDWING

#164 JAN '74

Parents are the ones who are there when you want to be alone with a date and nowhere to be found when you need five bucks.

—Alfred E. Neuman

#175 JUN '75

Ms. LIBERTY

ANOTHER
MAD
MINI-
POSTER

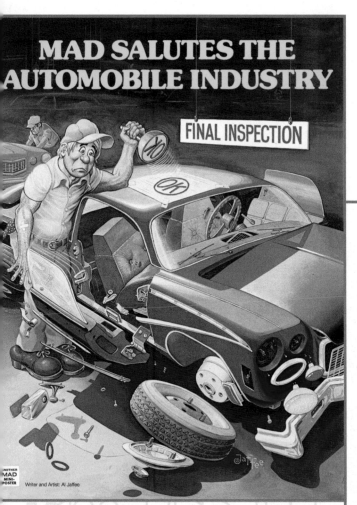

MAD SALUTES THE AUTOMOBILE INDUSTRY

FINAL INSPECTION

ANOTHER MAD MINI-POSTER
Writer and Artist: Al Jaffee

#190 APR '77

Politicians are always trying to convince you that they can solve the unemployment problem if you'll just give them a job.

—Alfred E. Neuman

#193 SEP '77

DON MARTIN DEPT. PART II

ONE WEDNESDAY EVENING IN A RESTAURANT MEN'S ROOM

EMPLOYEES MUST WASH HANDS BEFORE RETURNING TO WORK

ARTIST & WRITER: JOHN CALDWELL

#230 APR '82

GAMES FEEBLE PLAY DEPT.

MAD PASTIMES FOR THE BEDRIDDEN

ARTIST AND WRITER PAUL PETER PORGES

EAR WAX SCULPTURING

COTTON BALL GOLF

SUGAR CUBE TIDDLYWINKS

USED TISSUE BASKETBALL

MEDICATION SOCCER

MERCURY "SPACE SHOTS"

TOE MUPPETS

UNDER-THE-BED LINT SAILING REGATTAS

CHICKEN SOUP BLIND MAN'S BLUFF

BREAKFAST TRAY LIMBO

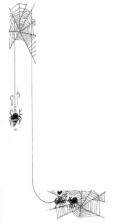

A judge is nothing more than a lawyer who's been benched.

Hey, gang! After ten years, it's time once again for MAD's nutty "Cliché Monster" game! Here's how it works: Take any familiar phrase or colloquial expression, give it an eerie gothic setting so you create a new type monster, and you're playing at

HORRIFYING CLICHÉS

ARTIST: PAUL COKER   WRITER: FRANK JACOBS

Driving A HARD BARGAIN

Hanging On To The BITTER END

Ducking An ISSUE

Weighing The ALTERNATIVES

Going Out With A BANG

Coming To A SCREECHING HALT

Losing One's VIRTUE

Bottling Up One's EMOTIONS

Throwing A TANTRUM

Opening An OLD WOUND

#248 JUL '84

GEORGE SLAVE-OWNER

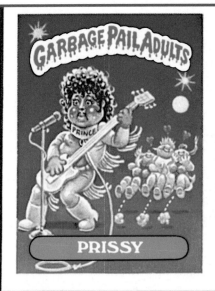

PRISSY

KHO MANIAC

DEAD MEESE

HOT AIR HELMS

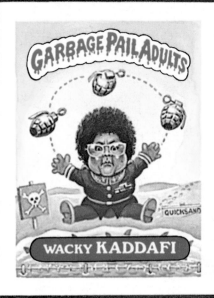

WACKY KADDAFI

BULLY BOTHA

YUCKY ARAFAT

MOUTHY McENROE

Artists: Will Elder and Harvey Kurtzman

#265 SEP '86

42

If you've ever flown, you know that every airline passenger is provided with reading material to help while away the time and make you forget how boring and uncomfortable the trip really is. This reading material usually consists of three items: (1) A magazine that extols the virtues of the airline you're flying, (2) A mail order catalogue of products that are sold by the airline you're flying, and (3) A safety information guide that makes you wish you'd never heard of the airline you're flying. With this idiotic article, we take

A MAD LOOK AT AIRLINE SAFETY INSTRUCTIONS

Airline emergency procedures look great...on paper!

SAFETY INFORMATION
INFORMATION DE SEGURIDAD
RENSIGNEMENTS POUR VOTRE SECURITÉ
ROISA RUCK

BOING FATBELLY
727 FEET (AROUND THE MIDDLE)

WRITER AND ARTIST: AL JAFFEE

HOW TO LOCATE THIS CARD

FORCED LANDING AT SEA PROCEDURE

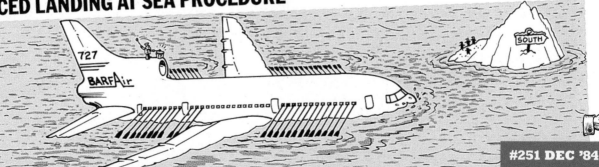

#251 DEC '84

But in real life, they wouldn't quite work out that way...

EMERGENCY LANDING POSITION

This is the position most passengers will probably assume!!

EMERGENCY EXITS

Diagrams of passengers heading for the exits always show an airliner with no seats, toilets, galleys, compartment walls, movie screens -- or people packed in like sardines!!

USING EMERGENCY OXYGEN

When three hundred oxygen masks drop down into a hysterical crowd, this is more like what you'll see!!

THE REAGAN

(with apologies to Edgar Allan Poe)

ARTIST: GERRY GERSTEN   WRITER: FRANK JACOBS

Once upon a cold November, back in '80, you'll remember,
*   Came to pass a great election, with a wondrous change in store;*
By a landslide, one was winning, promising a new beginning;
*   Tall and proud, he stood there, grinning, like so many times before;*
*   Who was he, this cool one, grinning, like so many times before?*
*   'Twas The Reagan, nothing more.*

Once he was inaugurated, Reaganomics he created,
*   Promising a balanced budget, like we had in days of yore;*
"Though," he said, "our debt is growing, and a bundle we are owing,
*   "I'll cut taxes, 'cause I'm knowing this will save us bucks galore;"*
*   "Please explain," a newsman asked, "how this will save us bucks galore?"*
*   Quoth The Reagan, "Less is more."*

Pushing for defense, he pleaded, brand-new missiles would be needed:
*   "That's the only way," he said, "to keep the country out of war;"*
"True," he said, "they're not required, and they're not meant to be fired;
*   "In five years they'll be retired—still we must build hundreds more;"*
*   "Tell us why," a newsman asked, "we must be building hundreds more?"*
*   Quoth The Reagan, " Jobs galore."*

Was he real or from a movie? "Make my day" sure sounded groovy,
*   Standing up to Congress or the rebels in El Salvador;*
Flicks like "Rambo" he promoted (sev'ral times, it should be noted);
*   Once John Wayne he even quoted, when Kaddafi threatened war;*
*   "Does this mean," a newsman asked, "we're heading toward a Mid-East war?"*
*   Quoth The Reagan, "Hit the shore."*

During times he wasn't dozing, many plans he was proposing,
*   Dealing with the deficit, which he no longer could ignore;*
"Cuts," he said, "I'm recommending, pending our ascending spending,
*   "With attending trends suspending, then extending as before."*
*   "Does this mean," a newsman asked, "a balanced budget like before?"*
*   Quoth The Reagan, "Nevermore."*

Gersten '86

If you live to 80, you're doing fine. If you live to 90, you've really beaten the odds. However, there are some among us who believe they'll live forever. We're referring to Mr. Clean, Cap'n Crunch and the rest of that copyrighted gang. Well, we've got some news for them! Eventually *everyone* dies, them included! So, to show them what's in store, we've prepared these...

OBITUARIES
For Merchandising Characters

FRED WHIPPLE DIES AT 54

Fred Whipple died today of suffocation after being squeezed to death under a truckload of toilet tissues. He was 54.

Whipple began his career at the Charmin Company as a sheet counter, and later became chief roll inspector and scent supervisor.

"We shall miss him greatly," said a Charmin spokesman. "After all, we have lost our Number Two man."

In accordance with Whipple's last request, his body will be wrapped in 5,000 squeezably soft sheets and placed on permanent display at a local supermarket.

Mr. Clean Dies at 33; Victim of Pollution

Mr. Clean died today after losing a fight with lung cancer. He was 33.

"He was a battler to the last," said his son-in-law, Brawny, "but the filthy air and polluted environment were too much for him."

During his final months, the once-muscular Mr. Clean wasted away to a shadow of his robust size. Despite his terminal illness, he poured himself into his work, continuing to attack his sworn enemies, grease, dirt and soot.

"We tried to keep him alive with ammonia transfusions," said a hospital spokesman, "but by then it was hopeless. Still, he fought to the last drop before throwing in the sponge.

In his will, Mr. Clean left his entire estate to the EPA, except for his ear ring, which he bequeathed to Miss Clairol.

Campbell Kids Die

Boris and Doris Campbell, famed for decades as the Campbell Soup Kids, died today within hours of each other.

Doctors at the scene believe both succumbed to the Smurf Disease, otherwise known as "acute cuteness."

ARTIST: BOB CLARKE
WRITER: FRANK JACOBS

PILLSBURY DOUGHBOY AN APPARENT SUICIDE

Poppin' Fresh, the Pillsbury Doughboy, is dead at 36, a probable suicide. His body was discovered early today in an unattended oven heated to 450°F.

According to a neighbor, Betty Crocker, who identified the body, Fresh had been suffering from depression. "He'd become very silent and withdrawn," Crocker said. "Nobody could get a rise out of him."

It is believed that the Doughboy first became depressed when he realized he hadn't grown an inch in more than 30 years. His outward cheerfulness apparently concealed a deep inferiority complex, which worsened with age.

"He was always so pitifully pale," said Crocker. "Now at least there's some color to him."

Funeral services will be held tomorrow at the Duncan Hines Funeral Home. Mourners may view the body, once it has been frosted.

Mr. Goodwrench Dies in Garage Accident

Mr. George Melvin (G.M.) Goodwrench, an auto mechanic, was crushed to death today when an '82 Buick Regal toppled from a faulty hydraulic lift.

According to a garage co-worker, Mr. Goodwrench had a history of being "accident-prone." In 1985, he was hospitalized after his head became entangled in a moving fan-belt. A year earlier, he narrowly survived after being sucked under in a grease pit.

At last report, Mr. Goodwrench's body remained trapped beneath the Buick Regal.

"We're jammed up just now," said a garage spokesman. "We'll get to him just as soon as there's someone available."

Morris the Cat Dies for the Ninth Time

Morris the cat is dead at 23. The famed finicky feline died of starvation following a 38-day, "Liver-or-else!" hunger strike.

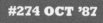

According to his veterinarian, Morris had apparently suffered eight previous deaths, but had "miraculously survived" each time. "The ninth was one too many," the doctor said.

A loner to the end, Morris had no close friends. There are several distant cousins—Heathcliff, Garfield, Felix, Tom, Sylvester and Bill, none of whom care to get involved.

Ronald McDonald Dies

Ronald McDonald is dead at 19. According to a distant relative, Herb, death was due to over-exposure.

A MAD LOOK AT DISNEY

CLASSICS

ARTIST & WRITER: SERGIO ARAGONES

Remember the movie "Saturday Night Fever" starring What's-his-name? It was about dancing! No? Hmm…

How about "Flashdance," that movie about dancing starring that girl who wasn't a good dancer so they had to use a stand-in for her? You remember that, don't you?

Ah hah! A glimmer of recognition flickers in your otherwise dull, uncomprehending eyes! Well, you can bet your twine collection the people who made this movie remember

It's so nice to go to a place where they serve you three meals a day!

Not if they're served at the same time!

Our socially conscious daughter thinks we should send this food to starving Asians!

We'd also have to send the Marines to make them eat it!

I think the folks baby you too much!

Yeah! But it's getting better! Last week I was finally taken off breast feeding!

What do you get with the breakfast special?

Gas!

This is such a corny 1940-is type picture

ARTIST: MORT DRUG

What are you doing here? Guests aren't allowed at staff parties! Get lost!

Just who do you think you're talking to?

Judging by your profile, I'd say Barbra Streisand's daughter!

CLICHÉ!: Rich girl meets boy from the wrong side of the tracks…

Bubbie, you have to concentrate on the music! That's all that matters! You have to feel the music and nothing else!

Not even your hand on my tush?

Not if you want to lose your inhibitions!

I think I'm going to lose more than my inhibitions before this dance is over!

CLICHÉ!: Repressed virgin discovers her sexuality…

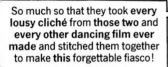

Dancing

So much so that they took **every lousy cliché** from **those two** and **every other dancing film ever made** and stitched them together to make **this** forgettable fiasco!

In fact, there are so many clichés here that we had to use a **special computer** to keep track of them!

Well, folks, that does it for my **opening monologue!** In the actual movie, my voice-over begins the film, then **leaves** and **never returns!** If the **audience** was **smart**, it would do the **same thing!** Mad readers have the same option—keep reading or pass right by...

t's why it's back in the s! That way the picture only **20 years** out of ate! If it was in the 0's it would've been 0 years out of date!

The waiters here are all **college men!** That one is studying to be a **lawyer** and that one is studying to be an **engineer**...

You need a fork? **Call my service!** I don't make **table calls!**

Hmmm, it's **obvious** what this one's **studying to be!**

It's your job to fool the guests into believing they're having a **good time!** Dance with their ugly wives and daughters, or else you're **fired!**

Gee, Max makes me **feel good!**

Really? Are you an **employee?**

No— an **anti-semite!**

DRUCKER

ER: STAN HART

Johnny, what am I going to do? I'm **pregnant!**

Don't worry, Pinhead! I wouldn't let **anything** bad happen to you!

I think you're a **little late** with **that promise!**

CLICHÉ!: The kindness of the less fortunate working class towards one another...

Bubbie, if I go for an **abortion**, I won't be able to dance with Johnny in the big **dance exhibition** next Saturday!

I can **take** your place!

No, I think I'd better go for the abortion myself!

I mean the **dance exhibition**, dummy!

Oh, yeah!

CLICHÉ!: Amateur steps in to perform for the ailing professional...

CLICHÉ!: Sequences showing klutzy student struggling to learn…

CLICHÉ!: Student falls in love with teacher…

CLICHÉ!: Klutz miraculously turns into graceful dancer overnight…

CLICHÉ!: Tension—will she succeed?

CLICHÉ!: Stand-in makes good…

CLICHÉ!: The guy senses that he's fallen in love with the girl without knowing it…

LICHÉ!: Hero accused unfairly…

CLICHÉ!: No guy is good enough for Daddy's little girl…

ICHÉ!: Dancing as foreplay…

CLICHÉ!: Typical sex scene with music, groping, and little else…

ICHÉ!: Sheltered, rich girl learns about life from street-wise, poor hero…

CLICHÉ!: Boy learns to have faith in himself…

CLICHÉ!: Girl stands up for her man at the cost of her reputation…

CLICHÉ!: The self-righteous, pompous displays a trace of humility…

CLICHÉ!: Father realizes his daughter is no longer a little girl…

CLICHÉ!: Impromptu dance turns into a slic choreographed production…

CLICHÉ!: The old folks feel the rhythm and join in with the kids…

CLICHÉ!: Leave the ending vague enough so that i bomb makes it, there can always be a se

The only time most people are modest is in describing their own faults.

ALONG THE SNIDE LINES DEPT.

Over the years, we here at MAD have discovered that nastiness is actually therapeutic. There's just something about hurling insults at self-satisfied celebrities and foolish fads that soothes the heart and cleanses the soul. No wonder we gleefully look forward to this dangerous moment when we relieve ourselves (mentally, that is) by spewing out...

the MAD NASTY FILE
VOLUME III

ARTIST: GERRY GERSTEN   WRITER: TOM KOCH

HULK HOGAN

...enables us to show the Iranians that our country can produce raving lunatics, too.
...markets a Hulk Hogan Doll that's an exact replica of himself—except it's smarter.
...made wrestling his career because he was afraid to take his chances in a competitive sport.

DAVID LETTERMAN

...avoids putting viewers to sleep by coming on the air after they're already asleep.
...may be the funniest man to come from Indianapolis since John Dillinger.
...smokes big, smelly cigars, but relies chiefly on his personality to drive people away.

#282 OCT '88

#290 OCT '89

TALES FROM THE DUCK SIDE DEPT.

THE DREADED DENTAL DEBACLE

DOCTOR MARROW, JANE CIANCI IS ON THE PHONE AND SHE'S...DOCTOR? DOCTOR MARROW?

OKAY, TELL HER I'LL *CALL HER BACK* AS SOON AS I'M *FINISHED* WITH THIS *ROOT CANAL,* BEVERLY!

ARTIST AND WRITER: DUCK EDWING

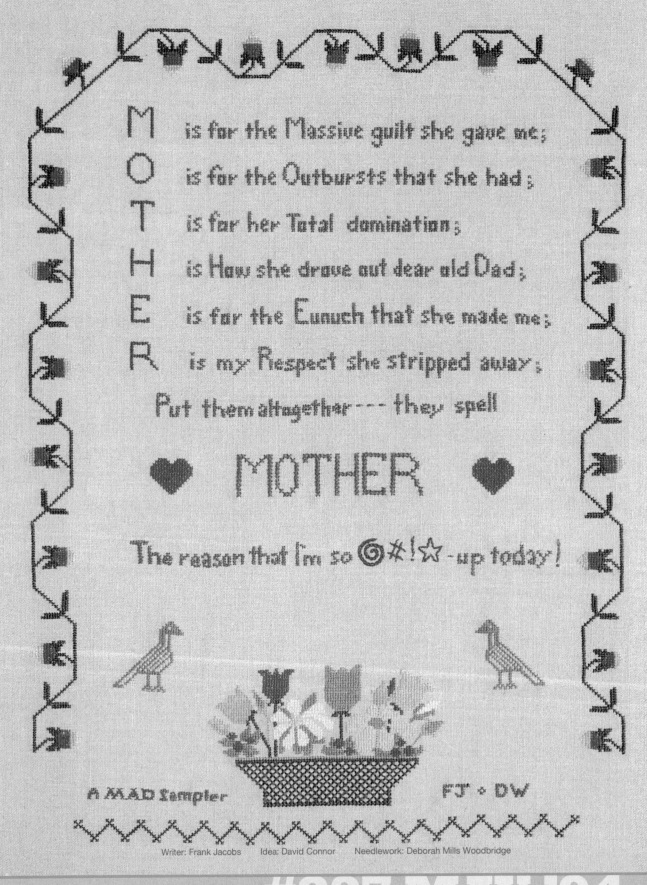

M is for the Massive guilt she gave me;

O is for the Outbursts that she had;

T is for her Total domination;

H is How she drove out dear old Dad;

E is for the Eunuch that she made me;

R is my Respect she stripped away;

Put them altogether--- they spell

♥ **MOTHER** ♥

The reason that I'm so ☺#!☆ -up today!

A MAD Sampler   FJ ◊ DW

Writer: Frank Jacobs   Idea: David Connor   Needlework: Deborah Mills Woodbridge

I'm **Will the Thrill**,..the **Strat-ford**..**ace**,
So better **lis-ten**..**up** good, 'cause I'm in..**your**..**face**;
The **play's**..the..**thing**, but they tell me, a-las,
That you **clods fall asleep** reading mine..in..**class**;
Well, I just..**found**..**out** what the world..**en-joys**,
So I've **borrowed**..**this**..**beat** from the **Beast-ie Boys**;
Is this..a..**rap-per**..that..you..see?
Gadzooks! Sure is, because the rap's..**on**..me!
I'm the **noblest show-man**..of..them..all,
And I've **given**..my..**gigs** an o-ver-**haul**;
Yea, the **game's a-foot,** and all the world's..a..**stage**
For the **sound** and the **fury** of this hot..**new**..**rage**;
A **bard** should be **made** of..**stern-er**..**stuff,**
So get up..to..**date** and Rap On,..**Mac-Duff!**
As…

Mad Raps Up Shakespeare

ARTIST: GEORGE WOODBRIDGE   WRITER: FRANK JACOBS

#300 JAN '91

The SOLILOQUY RAP from "HAMLET"

So what **do I do** when **life's**..**a**..**bitch**?
Should **I** be or **not be**—I **don't**..**know**..**which**!
Now you **may**..**be**..**thinkin'** I've **gone**..**insane**,
But you're **lookin'** at one **mel-an-chol-y**..**Dane**;
If I **packed**..**it**..**in**, I'd get **lots**..**of**..**Z's**;
And I wouldn't have to **count my cal-o-ries**;
I'd never **have**..**to**..**worry** what this **cas-tle**..**cost**;
Or 'bout **losin'**..**my**..**teeth** because I **nev-er flossed**;
There's **just**..**one**..**hang-up** that **bugs**..**me**,..**bub**—
I could **wind up dreamin'**, and there's..**the**..**rub**;
Bein' **dead**..**or alive**—either way..**I'm**..**screwed**;
As you **plainly can**..**see**, I'm one **mixed-up**..**dude**!

The BATTLEFIELD RAP from "RICHARD III"

A horse! A horse! I **need**..**one**..**bad**!
And I know **it's too late** to **place**..**an**..**ad**;
A horse! A horse! That's **all**..**I**..**need**;
I'd **swap**..**my**..**throne** for a **slightly used**..**steed**,
Or a **broken-down nag** that **pulls**..**a**..**plow**;
I'd **even con-sid-er** a **juiced-up**..**cow**,
Or, **fail-ing**..**that**, a **sheep**..**will**..**do**;
I'd **even look kindly** on a **kang-a-roo**,
Or an **ox** or a **camel** or a **slimmed-down**..**yak**
Or a **very large woman** with a **good**..**strong**..**bac**
If I've **nothing**..**to**..**ride**, you **have**..**my**..**word**
You can **say**..**good-bye to Richard**..**the Third**!

MARC ANTONY'S FUNERAL RAP from "JULIUS CAESAR"

Hey, **friends and Romans**, **Big Julie's been**..**hit**,
So **clean out**..**your**..**ears** while I **do**..**my**..**bit**;
He was **one**..**tough**..**dude**—the **town's**..**top**..**gun**,
And for **years in the charts** was **Num-ber**..**One**;
But **Brutus and his gang**..said, "We'll **wax**..**the**..**schmuck**
So they **took**..**a**..**stab** and **Big Julie**..**got**..**stuck**;
Now I **wantcha**..**to**..**know** that they're **sweet-ie**..**pies**,
Even though **some peo-ple** think **oth-er-wise**;
Sure they **dis'd**..**Big Julie**, **a-gain** and **a-gain**,
But we **know**..**the**..**swine** are **honor'ble men**;
No, they're **not**..**the**..**kind** that we **should**..**con-demn**,
Though you wouldn't want your **sis-ters** to **mar-ry**..**them**
And I'm **not sug-gest-ing** that you **wax**..**them**,..**too**,
Even though it **might**..**seem like the thing**..**to**..**do**;
But **if**..**you**..**should**, and the **rats**..**all**..**die**,
If you **need a new boss**, then **I'm**..**your**..**guy**!

The BALCONY RAP from "ROMEO AND JULIET"

Juliet baby, you're chill,..you're..rad!
If we got to-geth-er, we could make..it..bad!

Romeo honey, you've a real..smooth..line;
So what's the story—your place..or..mine?

Not so fast there, sweetie—let's..not..forget
I'm a Mon-ta-gue,..you're a Cap-u-let;

You're the Number One stud in this wack-wack..town!
Let's get..it..on before our bods..cool..down!

Both families hate the oth-er's..guts;
If we tied..the..knot,..they'd all..go..nuts!

If it busts..their..chops, they all..can..choke!
So hear..me..good—I ain't blow-in'..smoke!

You know that we'll wind..up..dead,..of..course;

Well, dying's..no..kick,..but it beats..di-vorce!

The Capulets
227

THE BELCHING DRAGON

CHINESE FOOD to EAT IN or TAKE OUT

Free
can soda
with orders
over
$100.00

50 lbs.
white rice
with
every order

SOUPS

Dropped Egg Soup 1.75
★ One Ton Soup 1.75
Hot & Scalding Soup 2.25
Ten Ingredients Water 3.25
Sweet and Salmonella Soup 2.95
Chinese Fire Drill Soup 2.50
★ Happy Bacteria Cup 2.50

APPETIZERS

Steam-Cleaned Dumplings 3.95
Burn Your Tongue Platter 8.95
Barbecued Bear Ribs 6.30
Scallion Cow Pancakes (for two) 2.95
MSG with Orange Flavor 4.95

NOODLES

★ Cellophane Noodles with
 Styrofoam Peanuts 5.50
Cold Noodles in Sesame Waste 3.50
Some Glum Noodles 8.25
No Fun Noodles 4.75

PORK

New Shoe Pork 6.75
Roasted Pork in Shriner Hat 6.95
Recently Shampooed Pork 6.95
Andrew Diced Pork 9.75
Roast Pork Puppy Chow 7.25
Porky Pig Cartoonese Style 7.50
Pork And Mindy 6.75

★ May Not Be Edible

VEGETABLES

★ Broccoli in Human Sauce 5.95
Shredded Documents with Peking Sauce ..5.25
Bean Crud with Special Rotting Fungus ..6.25
Snow Shovel with Peas 7.75
Egg Neil Young 4.95
Green Beans with Black Bean Sauce ..4.95
Black Beans with Green Bean Sauce ..5.95
Eggplant Prepared Under
 Mysterious Circumstances 5.95
★ Baby Corn with Adoption Papers ...4.95
Vegetables with Tingling Horse Flavor ..5.50

POULTRY

San Diego Chicken with Pine Tar 6.25
Battering Ram Chicken 6.25
Peking Daffy Duck 7.50
★ Lemon Pledge Chicken 6.25
Amazing Talking Chicken 8.75
Tongue Licked Duck 7.50
★ Chicken & Grief 6.25
Duck Edwing Prepared in
 Questionable Taste 6.25
Chicken Escaping With Wings 7.75
Mocked Duck 7.25
General Schwarzkopf Chicken 6.75
Goofy Grinning Chicken 6.75
Innocent Bystander Chicken 6.25
Moo Goo Guy Williams 8.75
Moo Goo Guy Molinari 8.25
Moo Goo Guy Pan & Teller
 In Disappearing Sauce 4.50

BEEF

Air-Dropped Beef 6.85
Double Chin Beef 6.85
★ Beef with More Beef 7.75
Carnage of Beef 6.85
Sizzling Wanton Beef 4.95
Beef And Dried Pepper
 Spilled on Lap 9.25
Beef with Bad News 8.85
★ Great Barrier Beef 4.95
★ What's Your Beef 5.50

SEAFOOD

Squished Eel Delight 8.50
Shrimp with Alibi 8.25
★ Young Dead Fish 9.25
Crispy Fish with Discarded Needle ..9.95
Prawns in L.L. Bean Sauce 7.50
Aromatic Octopus On Wheels 10.50
Force Fed Shrimp 7.75
★ Flounder with Water Pistol 8.95

CHEF'S SPECIALS

★ Sesame Street Duck 11.75
 Choice chunks of undernourished fowl
 pulled with waterchestnuts and stir-fried
 in a sizzling wok by popular Muppets.

Overpriced Happy Family 14.25
 Scallops, crabmeat and psychotropic
 mushrooms sautéed with fresh chef's
 thumbs and served on a Sealy
 Posturpedic.

★ Tienanmen Square Beef 17.75
 Oppressed young beef, severely battered,
 crushed with bamboo shoots and
 brutally smothered as you watch from
 your take on a big screen.

Health Inspector's Seafood
 Delight .... FREE!
 Fresh lobster, shrimp and prawns
 expertly prepared in the classic Mexican
 restaurant down the block, brought in
 through our back door and served with a
 crispy fifty dollar bill rolled in a napkin.
 (Must be ordered in advance.)

Cashier will
change shirt
at your request.

DESSERTS

Unfortunate Cookies 2.50
Sweet Fried Rodents 3.95
Ice Cream with Garlic Sauce 3.95
Boneless Pudding 2.75
Chicken Almond Ring Ding 3.50

WRITERS: JOE RAIOLA AND CHARLIE KADAU   ARTIST: GEORGE WOODBRIDGE

#322 OCT '93

GREAT MOMENTS IN HISTORY

Washington Cross-Dressing the Delaware

#326 MAR/APR '94

Anyone who's read the comic pages surely has delighted to the happy-go-lucky antics of Billy, Jeffy, Dolly and P.J., who prove that the wonder of childhood is like a precious diamond, with all the sparkle and all the rough edges that make. . .oh, who are we kidding? When does the strip take place, 1953? Dad has the only paycheck in the house, somehow supports five people and three pets, and still has time off for school plays, vacation, and games of catch? The biggest problem this family ever had was when P.J. got scared by the giraffe! It's time we showed these 58-year-old first graders what life is really like in. . .

the DYSFUNCTIO

MONDAY

"See, Jeffy, I told ya-- just like cable!"

TUESDAY

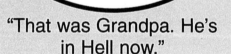

"That was Grandpa. He's in Hell now."

WEDNESDAY

"Mommy! Mommy! P.J. found the gun!"

THURSDAY

"You made this card all by yourself? It sucks!"

FAMILY CIRCUS

ARTIST: GEORGE WOODBRIDGE
WRITER: DESMOND DEVLIN

FRIDAY

"If you loved your fish as much as he loved you, maybe he wouldn't have died."

SATURDAY

"Billy will be ready as soon as he's finished changing the bed sheets he wet last night."

SUNDAY

#333 JAN/FEB '95

There's a lot to be said for brevity.

If NORMAN ROCKWELL DEPICTED THE 90'S
"LAST PARKING SPACE AT THE MALL"

#351 NOV '96

#352 DEC '96

TALES FROM THE DUCK SIDE DEPT.

THE RAUNCHY RESTROOM REVULSION

ARTIST AND WRITER: DUCK EDWING

HERE'S EXCITING NEWS!!!

PSYCHIC FIENDS NETWORK®, the original psychic line that has helped more than 10 million obtain higher phone bills, is introducing the

SPECIAL PSYCHIC FIENDS PHONE HOTLINE

The Psychic Fiends Network® is a worldwide legend. By far the most successful and acclaimed psychic line not yet shut down by a government agency! More Americans turn

"The ff-ff—irst t—ttt-hing ttthe psychic tt—tttold me, wwwaasssss ttthaatt I-I-I s-s-stuttered...a-and sshee ddddoesn't eeven k-k-know mmm-me! AA-AAA-Amazzing!"

NEED PROOF? READ ON!

Famous paid celebrities boast about our services. Our own spokespeople will tell you how wonderful Psychic Fiends Network® is! And Ms. Dionne Wartlick, our founder and single largest stockholder, is our biggest supporter! This respected recording artist is making more money with us than she ever did with her old, saccharine-sweet records.

Dozens of other successful celebrities have had their careers really take off since using the Psychics Fiends Hotline, including former stars of *The Love Boat* and *What's Happening!!* Of course, to mention

lawn care tips or how to get that ugly stain out of your carpet. At $3.99 per minute, no subject is too difficult or trivial for our Master Psychics.

HOW DO I KNOW THE ADVICE I GET IS GOOD?

Because our Master Psychics don't make snap judgments or decisions! After you ask us something, we think, we mull, we confer, we contemplate, we ponder, we deliberate. Often our Master Psychics go into deep trances, which could last 10, 20, 30 minutes or longer. While attaining this higher plane of consciousness, it may sound like you are being put on hold, or that they are taking another call from someone else or have simply gone out on a lunch break. But don't be fooled and above all DON'T

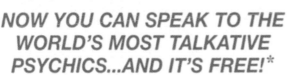

NOW YOU CAN SPEAK TO THE WORLD'S MOST TALKATIVE PSYCHICS...AND IT'S FREE!*

to the Psychic Fiends Network® than all other psychic, guidance or astrology lines combined. Every day we receive thousands of calls from everyday people — government workers, teachers, office workers — virtually anyone whose employer hasn't blocked their access to 1-900 numbers!

The second you call us, we'll start telling you things about yourself. Personal things, such as how gullible you are and how you need to get a life!

As we build your confidence and keep you on the phone longer and longer, we'll tell you life-shattering things, such as if you have an incurable disease, whether your mate is cheating on you, who might want to see you dead and when and if you'll be totally disfigured in a car crash. Of course, all of our life-shattering predictions are for AMUSEMENT PURPOSES ONLY!

WE'RE ALWAYS AS CLOSE AS YOUR TELEPHONE

We know you have concerns day and night, so we're here 24 hours a day, 7 days a week. You can call us as often as your credit card or long distance carrier allows!

Washed-up recording star Ms. Dionne Wartlick had no future until she stumbled into the Psychic Fiends Network business.

them by name would mean we'd have to compensate them, and you don't have to be psychic to know we don't want to do that!

WHAT CAN I ASK ABOUT?

Ask about love, romance, career, job, health, money — hell, we don't even care if you ask about recipe shortcuts,

HANG UP! We want to be sure you get the right information, and we don't care how long it takes.

(In order to call, you must be 18 years or older, or have access to a valid credit card that belongs to someone 18 years or older. Under 18, please pretend you are over 18 and we'll pretend we're not psychic and don't know your real age!)

Remember, this is a **FREE READING!** We'll read to you from the newspaper, *TV Guide*, maybe a phone book. But if you want psychic predictions, now you're talking money! **Call today!**

(*you pay just for the call, the words spoken are FREE!)

A MAD AD PARODY

MONROE &

It's painful-childhood-memory-time!
Meet your newest best buddy Monroe, and
join him on an angst-ridden teenage adventure!

...this is Kathy Rugby for Free-Stay Maxi Pads...

That reminds me, Monroe — run down to the market and fetch me some tampons!

YIPES!

Um, where are the —

Hi, Monroe! Are you going to the dance tonight? Maybe you and I could... oh...

..THE CURSE

ARTIST: BILL WRAY   WRITER: ANTHONY BARBIERI

#356 APR '97

Community Chest

FALSE RUMOR ABOUT YOUR COMPANY SUPPORTING SATANISM HITS INTERNET

Lose $550 Million

© 1997 PORKER BROTHERS, INC.

Chance

ADVANCE TOKEN TO WHITE HOUSE COFFEE KLATCH

Pay $250,000

© 1997 PORKER BROTHERS, INC.

Chance

TOP EXECUTIVE TERMINATED AFTER 10 MONTHS

Pay Golden Parachute Compensation Package of $75 Million

© 1997 PORKER BROTHERS, INC.

CHAIRMAN OF THE BOARD GAME DEPT.

What is the deal with Monopoly? How can it still be best selling board game in the world when it's become dated that it has absolutely nothing to do with the way

MONOPO

That Reflect The Way b

Community Chest

COMPANY CITED FOR RUNNING OVERSEAS CHILD SWEATSHOP

Hire P.R. Firm to Spin Story and Control Damage Pay $20 Million

© 1997 PORKER BROTHERS, INC.

Chance

HIRE NBA STAR TO ENDORSE YOUR SHODDY PRODUCT

Pay $18 Million

© 1997 PORKER BROTHERS, INC.

Community Chest

EXPAND INTO SMALL TOWN AND DRIVE MOM & POP STORES OUT OF BUSINESS

Collect $50 Million

© 1997 PORKER BROTHERS, INC.

walmart
OPEN FOR BUSINESS

candy shop
CLOSED

Chance

FRIVOLOUS LAWSUIT FILED AGAINST COMPANY

Pay $7 Million in Out-of-Court Settlement

© 1997 PORKER BROTHERS, INC.

Community Chest

NAFTA SIGNING ALLOWS YOU TO CLOSE U.S. FACTORY AND MOVE IT TO MEXICO

Collect $49 Million Additional Profits

© 1997 PORKER BROTHERS, INC.

Chance

THREATEN TO MOVE COMPANY OUT OF CITY

Collect $9 Million in Tax Breaks

© 1997 PORKER BROTHERS, INC.

eball corporate fat cats of America conduct business y? Isn't it about time Parker Brothers woke up and signed this thing? Ah, why wait for them? Here's MAD's...

Y CARDS
ss Is REALLY Done Today

ARTIST: SAM VIVIANO   WRITER: J. PRETE

Community Chest

OPEN FLASHY WEBSITE ON INTERNET TO PROMOTE YOUR PRODUCTS

Lose $1 Million

© 1997 PORKER BROTHERS, INC.

INTERNET SALES

Chance

BUST UNION AND HIRE SCABS AT HALF THE SALARY

Collect $35 Million in Additional Profits

© 1997 PORKER BROTHERS, INC.

Community Chest

ANNOUNCE MASSIVE LAYOFFS IN DOWNSIZING MOVE

Stock Price Soars Collect $70 Million Bonus

© 1997 PORKER BROTHERS, INC.

Community Chest

TURN INFORMER IN INSIDER TRADING CASE

Get Out of Jail Free

© 1997 PORKER BROTHERS, INC.

Chance

TV NEWS SHOW EXPOSES CRIMINAL ACTIVITY IN YOUR COMPANY

Sue for Invasion of Privacy Collect $7 Million

© 1997 PORKER BROTHERS, INC.

#361 SEP '97

71

When it comes to the lack of cleanliness at public urinals,
it's amazing what some guys will stand for!

 **THE GENERATION CRAP DEPT.**

ARTIST: RICK TULKA   WRITER: RUSS COOPER

Generations come and generations go, and with each change of an era comes challenging personal and social issues, revolutions, rebellions and an idealist youth culture. The Sixties brought Vietnam, Kent State, LBJ, while the Nineties, well...let's just say the times they are a' changin' as MAD contrasts the...

60's AND THE 90's

VOICES OF A GENERATION:

60's SIMON & GARFUNKEL   **90's BEAVIS & BUTT-HEAD**

60's *Free Love*   90's *$2.99-per-minute Love*

60's *Tune in, turn on, drop out...*

90's *Rent it, view it, rewind it...*

#356 APR '97

75

It has been known to happen to doctors, lawyers, athletes, politicians and high powered Wall Street Execs. But there is nothing more disturbing than...

WHEN PR

SLOPPY EXORCISMS

NO-WIN BINGO

DRIVE-BY BAPTISMS

ESTS GO BAD

ARTIST: JOHN CALDWELL
WRITER: MIKE MAY

OLY WATER BALLOON FIGHTS

QUESTIONABLE CHARITIES

BISHOP'S HAT KEEP-AWAY

PRODUCT PLACEMENT IN SERMONS

EMPLOYING "WHEEL OF ABSOLUTION" TO DETERMINE PENANCE

HEAR THE RADIO THAT WOKE UP AN ENTIRE INDUSTRY*

*To the fact that there are idiots out there willing to spend hundreds of dollars just for a radio!

Popular Audio wrote that it is "a sonic masterpiece." *Radio Magazine* wrote that it is "simply amazing...a genuine break-through in sound quality!" And *High Fidelity* wrote, "Sorry, but you'll have to take thousands of dollars in advertising in *our* magazine like you did in *Popular Audio* and *Radio Magazine* before we'll write hyped-up copy about how great your radio is." What radio are they all talking about? The Boose® Wavy radio.

HALF A MILLION PEOPLE ALREADY OWN THE BOOSE® WAVY RADIO.

In just over three years, the Wavy radio has changed the way half a million people listen to music — people like Stanley Karpinski of Staten Island, NY, who said, "It's changed the way I listen to music. I stopped listening to CDs and audiocassettes! I had to! The Wavy won't play them. It's just a damn radio!"

OUR EXCLUSIVE, AWARD-WINNING DESIGN

The secret to the Wavy radio's remark-able success lies in an exclusive, award-winning design. Our experts spent countless hours designing sleek, elegant ads for the Wavy radio, resulting in a remarkably suc-cessful ad cam-paign that has won numerous awards for its design. The actual design of the radio itself

Open up a Wavy radio and you'll see our exclusive acoustic wavyguide speaker technology. You'll also immediately void our 30-day money back guarantee.

was a piece of cake, using the same technology found in a $9 K-Mart clock radio. The Wavy radio measures just 4 1/2" x 14" x 8 1/4" x 10"x 22 1/8" x 9". It comes with a credit card-sized remote control that will easily slip between the tightest of sofa cush-ions never to be seen again, six AM/FM pre-set buttons that have been perma-nently set at the factory to our favorite stations for

This miniature remote control was lost forever right after this photo was taken.

your convenience, and dual alarms which can be heard up to five miles away. Is it any wonder that people who weren't smart enough to buy a stereo system with a CD player, AM/FM radio, dual cassette deck, graphic equalizer and detachable speakers (for half the price that our product costs) are now stuck using the Boose® Wavy as their primary stereo system?

EVEN OUR IN-HOME TRIAL SOUNDS GREAT.

Order a Wavy radio today and take advantage of our risk-free, in-home trial. If after 30 days, you aren't con-vinced that this is the best sounding radio you've ever heard, simply return the radio to us in its original unopened carton for a full refund. No questions asked! That's right! You have our 100% guarantee that our in-home trial sounds great, providing you don't go back and reread this last paragraph for finely-crafted legal loopholes.

CALL TODAY AND MAKE SIX INTEREST-FREE PAYMENTS.

The Wavy radio is available for $349 direct from Boose®, one of the leading names in high fidelity equipment manu-facturers when listed alphabetically. And now our six-month installment payment plan lets you make six monthly payments interest free when you agree to our exclusive seventh payment of all interest! Call today and hear more about the product that has consumer groups and state attorneys general talking.

CALL BY NOVEMBER 1, 1998 and ask our operators about **FREE SHIPPING** and why we don't offer it.

CALL 1-800-BAMBOOZLED EXT. R2D2

When you call, ask about our six-month installment payment plan. (Qualifications based on a sworn affidavit that you own a valid credit card and that your call is not being traced or recorded by law enforcement officials.) Also ask about FedEx® delivery service and how it differs from the third rate carrier we'll be using to ship your radio.

Please specify your color choice:
☐ Barry White ☐ Earl Gray

Mr./Mrs./Ms.

Name _____ (Please Do Not Print)

Address

City _____ State _____ Zip

( )
Morning Phone

( )
Afternoon Phone

( )
Late Afternoon Phone

Evening Phone
(No Salesman will call.)

Mail to Boose® Corporation, Dept. NOCD-RU-NUTS The Compound on The Mountain, FramedAgain, MA 00019

Better sounding ads through research®

WRITER: JOHN FICARRA

A MAD AD PARODY

#371 JUL '98

78

MONICAGATE
THE NEVER-ENDING SAGA

Sinister villains, classic confrontations, hideous creatures, and yes, even a princess — albeit one with a thonged butt the size of Nebraska. The White House scandal had all the elements of a sci-fi epic, except one — there were no heroes.

STARR WARS

Not so long ago, in a country not so far away...

ARTIST: MARK STUTZMAN

#377 JAN '99

79

It was a time of ill tidings. Good men fell, and great woe and calamity shrouded the realm. And nowhere was the scourge more bleak, or the disaster more vast, than in the land of New Line Cinema! Many disasters at the box office nearly put them in the land of perpetual darkness. Just as there seemed to be no future for New Line or its bottom line, a single shaft of hope pierced the gloom. Nay, not one shaft of light, but THREE! A trilogy of movies sure to entice every fantasy-hungry role player, isolated mouth-breather and embittered loser in the land to make the arduous trek to the cineplex again, and again, and still again! Hopefully the fortunes of New Line would be restored, but only if a wary public did not become…

Why did they **choose me** to play **Dodo Gaggings?** Obviously, it **wasn't** for my **talent** as an **actor!** The **director** needed to find the **right person** to portray a **Slobbit** who is **3 feet, 6 inches tall!** After they put **2-inch lifts** in my **shoes,** we were in **business!** You've **never** seen a **lead character** like me! I may be the **first action-adventure hero** in **movie history** who could get his **ass kicked** by Harry Potter!

On the **other hand,** I made my **reputation** as **one** of the **finest Shakespearean actors** and have been **nominated** for an **Academy Award!** As **Gandoof,** I wear a **fake beard** and **silly hat** and **play** the **part** of a **great magician** rather **convincingly!** Watch closely as my **credibility** as an actor **totally disappears** before your **eyes!**

I'm **Peppercorn,** but some call me **Spider!** Others call me **Longstinks,** the **Renuzit, Elfdro**... or **Telemundo!** I've got more **stupid extra names** than P. Did... and the **Wu-Tang Clan combine**... What I **don't** have is a **decent** **shampoo** and **conditioner!**

ARTIST: HERMANN MEJIA
WRITER: DESMOND DEVLIN

As **Spam Gangrene,** I'm **chief tagalong nebbish** and **sidekick!** I'm **dim-witted,** **afraid** to **talk** to **girls** and an **all-around nothing —** in **other words,** I'm **this** film's **target audience!** If **I wasn't** in this **movie,** I'd be **first** on **line** to see it!

We're **Pimple** and **Baggybuns,** the **two most incompetent Slobbits** around! Give either of us **half** a **chance,** and we'll **stick** our **foot** in our **mouths!**

Which **ain't easy** when you're a **size 78 Wide!**

I'm **Billboard Gaggings,** oldest living **Slobbit!** On the **outside,** I appear to be a **friendly, happy-go-lucky fellow!** But **everybody** can **see** that just **beneath** the **cheery surface,** I'm **really** a **twisted, bitter, jealous,** desperately **unhappy dwarf!** Just like **Billy Crystal!**

As **Argon,** the **immorta**... **Elf princess,** people ask me, was it **hard findin**... the **inspiration** to **play a bizarre ancient characte**... who goes on **forever?** Actually, it came **easy** to me! My **dad** is **Steven Tyl**... from **Aerosmith!**

RED OF THE RINGS

EEBLE SCHTICK of KA-CHING!

I am **Borderline**, and I am **valiant, strong** and **brave**! I have **pledged** my **life** against **evil**, in **hopes** that I can **return** to my **homeland**, which **has** been completely **burned** and **destroyed**! I **said** I was **valiant, strong** and **brave**... I **never** said I was **smart**!

As you can **see** from my **bow**, I am the **archer Legolamb**! My **archery** skills are **unsurpassed**! My **acting** skills? Let's **put** it **this** way, I'm so **off target** I've **hit** the **screen** of the next **cineplex**! Tom Cruise's **butt** in *Vanilla Sky*, to be **exact**!

Behold **Aspercreme**, the bad guy **wizard** with a serious **wand** up his **butt**! **Gandoof** never **realized** that I was on the **side** of **evil**! He **should** have **gotten** a **clue** when I **pulled** a **rabbit** out of my **hat** and immediately **put** it into a **blender**! I hate **Gandoof** for his **naive faith** in **goodness**, and also because his **facial hair** is **two inches longer** than mine! **Size** does **count**, even in the **wizard world**!

I may **look** like something that got **coughed** up by a **400-pound** cat, but I'm **Gimmicki**, the angry dwarf! How do I **figure** in all this **confusion**? I'm **waiting** for someone to **tell** me! I'm **not sure** if I **appear** in this **segment** or **either** of the **next** two they **filmed**!

You're **lucky**! I **know** I **appear** in this **episode**, but as **one** of the **Dorcs**, the allegedly **deadly creatures** in **service** of **Sorehead's evil desires**, we have a **higher mortality rate** than **sitcoms** on the **WB**!

As **Galapagos**, the all-knowing **elf queen**, I'm the **wisest character** of **all**! And to **stand out** even more, **notice** how I'm **backlit**! Like someone in a **feminine hygiene commercial**!

Eh! Eh! Me am **Golfclub**, and me have been **driven insane**! **Not** by **Ring**, by this **cockamamie three-hour butt-blistering movie**! Look at this **splash page**! Talk about **endless**! And it **only** includes the **main characters**! Characters? It was **easier** to keep the **dogs straight** in *101 Dalmatians*!

#416 APR '02

I'm [s]orry we [to]ok the [m]ain [r]oad [a]nd got you [c]aught!

And that we tried to float the raft away, leaving **you** to get killed!

And how in the **bar**, we told **everybody** who you **really** were!

Not to mention the **campfire** that we set **attract-ed** the horse-men, and **you** almost died!

That's **okay.** But would you mind **not** leaning on my **bad** shoulder?

See? I **told** you **this** little creep holds grudges!

You'd **give** up your **immortality** to **marry** me? **What** made you decide?

We're about **90 minutes** into an **eight-hour trilogy,** and already it feels like a **lifetime!** Suddenly "forever" doesn't **seem** like such a **great** thing!

We've got to **[st]and together** to **stop** Sorehead!

Sorehead is getting **more powerful** by the **minute!**

Soon, Sorehead will **strike!**

Uh...does it strike **anyone** as strange that the **#1 bad guy** in this movie isn't actually **IN** this movie?

Dodo, I want you to have **this.** It's magic Slobbit chain mail that will **protect** you from **harm!**

Nice timing! The only way this gift could **matter more** to me is if I'd gotten it back in the Shire! You know, like **BEFORE** I got **stabbed?**

By **hiking** across this **mountain,** we'll **sneak** into Torpor unobserved!

Yeah, who could **EVER** spot **nine black silhouettes** doing two miles an hour against 400 miles of **pure white** snow? Shrewd!

Listen to this **ancient book**! It describes the dwarf army's **final moments!** "*The dwarves fought bravely, but were overwhelmed by numbers. The dorcs broke through the dwarf position and entered the chamber. Arghh! I was cut through by a dorc! My blood flowed freely! My heart came to a halt! And then I died – of boredom, as will be the fate of all who continue this endless quest!*"

That's so **sad,** yet **powerful!**

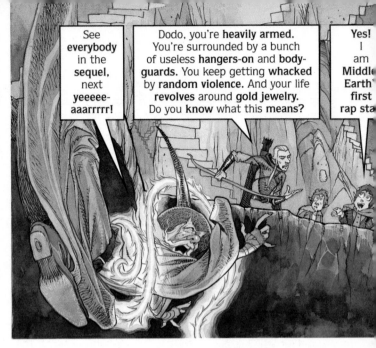

the BUNION

a.v. club — B-list celebrity interviews! | **store** — Wacky non-sequitur T-shirts! | **subscriptions** — Pay for stuff you get here for free! | **books** — Pay for old, free stuff!

VOLUME 38 ISSUE 43 — **AMERICA'S PHONIEST NEWS SOURCE** — [Search]

Front Page — Previous Issue — Archive

IN THE NEWS

Funny Hairdo, Muppet Reportedly Turns Otherwise Uninteresting Bush Photo "Wacky"

Above: President Bush, seen here sporting a comically oversized woman's hairdo while standing next to popular children's character Grover, was in fact standing alone and had a traditionally short, conservative men's hairstyle at the time the actual photo was taken.

NEW YORK, NY — The additions of a funny hairdo and a Muppet have turned what many referred to as an uninteresting photo of President Bush into a hilariously "wacky" image. The original photograph, released last Monday, was downloaded from the official White House website. With the use of a standard computer graphics program, a bouffant hairdo was digitally added to his head. Pasted into the photo is an image of popular Muppet character Grover, who appears to be standing next to Bush. "We made the photo so wacky that we almost didn't need to write our usual overly-long and one-note gag news story to accompany it," laughed Bunion editor Tom Koehler.

Unlikely Words, Phrases In Headline and Body of Story Make Some Articles Sorta Funny, Experts Say

ST. LOUIS, MO — A study issued by the Conference of American Journalism says that the simple act of using "a few well-chosen words can maybe turn a dry news story with, like, little humor potential, into one that's sorta funny. "It's a delicate balance," says panel spokesman Todd Aberline. "You've got to use a certain amount of standard news jargon but then every few lines, throw in a ringer." Experts note that you've totally got to watch the placement of the quotation marks as well, or you're screwed. "You definitely don't want to put your quotes around the incongruent word or phrase," Aberline explains. "That makes it look like you're quoting someone and that you, as the reporter, know the word wouldn't normally appear in that context in a standard newspaper article otherwise." According to the study, without the quotation marks, a really lame story can end up being pretty frickin' funny, and also way cool.

CRAPshot

A look at yet another rip-off of Letterman's Top Ten

The Most Overused Themes On Our Website

1. Subject of article vaguely referred to as "Some Guy" in the headline
2. Offensive, sacrilegious news story featuring Christ as a normal person who just happens to live among us
3. Headline peppered with gratuitous curse words as the entire set-up and execution of a gag
4. News item about a well-known advertising character saying and doing things its corporate owners would not approve of
5. Typical advice feature attributed to an unlikely columnist who disregards the questions entirely and instead replies to each letter by expounding on his, her, or its area of expertise, literary style, or obsession
6. Thinly-veiled "humorous" take on a horrific tragedy done sooner after the actual event than good taste would dictate

TOP STORY

Area Man Finds Headline Amusing But That's About It

Above: Legal assistant Ray Jeffries often finds the headlines amusing, but the bodies of the articles lacking in substance. "The captions they run below the photos aren't much better," he says.

BETHESDA, MD — Ray Jeffries thought the headline to this story was kind of funny, but "that was about it." Jeffries, a legal assistant at a local law firm, admits to having become bored by what he describes as an "entirely predictable format." "The headline was kind of amusing, I guess. But then the article was just a rehash of the headline. What's the point?"

Jeffries noted that it's not the first time he's had this reaction and that he previously chuckled at headlines involving the aging pope, a kindergarten class's bean sprout project and the Kool-Aid Man. "But basically it's all the same," he explains. "They shoot their wad with the headline and it's a lot of nothing after that." The 36-year-old considers himself a "fairly intelligent" person with a "reasonably good" sense of humor. "It's not that I don't get it. I can grasp subtlety. And I understand satire. But what more is there to say after you've led with, say, 'Ticketed Motorist Vows To Exact Revenge On Meter Maid With Caustic Barb In Memo Line Of Check'? That's the whole gag. Anything more is mere repetition."

OPINION

Point-Counterpoint: Point-Counterpoint

We've Kind Of Run This Feature Into The Ground, If You Ask Me

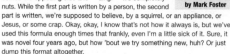

by Mark Foster

You know, these debates were funny at first. But they've become very predictable. And here's why: Generally, the first viewpoint puts forth a reasonable, logical argument in favor or in support of something, anything, whatever. Fine. All straight lines. Very dry. That's the set-up. Then comes the opposing side and — zing! — it's completely nuts. While the first part is written by a person, the second part is written, we're supposed to believe, by a squirrel, or an appliance, or Jesus, or some crap. Okay, okay, I know that's not how it always is, but we've used this formula enough times that frankly, even I'm a little sick of it. Sure, it was novel four years ago, but how 'bout we try something new, huh? Or just dump this format altogether.

Oh, Come On! I'm An Egg Separator, For God's Sake! That Right There Is Funny!

by An Egg Separator

Look, I'm an inanimate object and I'm delivering the opposing viewpoint to your argument! Don't you get it? It's frickin' hilarious! I can't really talk or think, nor do I have the physical ability to puts words on the page or computer screen. But that doesn't change the fact that here I am, arguing against your position and telling you that, yes, these debates are incredibly funny! Why? Because I'm a kitchen utensil, and not only do I have an opinion, but apparently it's such a strong opinion that I feel compelled to respond to you by totally flying off the handle! That's hilarious! A plastic doo-dad from your junk drawer actually getting upset! Instead of pitting your lame-ass argument against the rants of another person, the rebuttal is being written by me, (once again) an EGG SEPARATOR. Too damn funny!

EDITORIAL

Why Running An Editorial Attributed To Someone You Wouldn't Expect To Be Writing An Editorial On A Trivial Subject That Normally Doesn't Warrant An Editorial Is So Damn Funny Week After Week
by Nelson Mandela

ARTIST: SCOTT BRICHER   WRITER: SCOTT MAIKO
PHOTOS: IRVING SCHILD & AP/WIDE WORLD PHOTOS

OTHER NEWS

Some Guy In Mall Signs A Release To Pose For Picture To Run With Possibly Unflattering Mock News Story

Thirty Column Inches Of Text Used To Describe Fictional Middle-Class Woman In Dull Job Facing Uninteresting Dilemma, Maybe About Minor Nuisance In Break Room At Work Or Something

Ending Crazy Headline With Some Variation Of "Study Shows" Ensures Hilarity, Study Shows

Report: Starting Bizarre Headline With "Report" Apparently Even More Hilarious Than Ending With "Study Shows"

Retarded, Crippled People Head List Of Easy Targets For Zany Mock Articles For Third Consecutive Year

NEWS IN BRIEF

Inconsequential Everyday Occurrence Covered With Gravity, Detachment

BOULDER, CO — An inconsequential everyday occurrence was covered today with the gravity and detachment normally associated with a serious, substantial news item.

Jim Grout, a one-hour photo service employee, got a particularly bad static electricity shock when touching his bedroom doorknob after shuffling back from the bathroom at approximately 2:37 this morning. "Son-of-a-bee, it really woke me up," Grout, 51, told reporters. "I was half-asleep, then zap! Talk about a rude awakening."

Despite the noise of the shock seeming "very loud" to Grout, his wife, Kay, 49, slept undisturbed through the ordeal. "I had no idea anything happened until he mentioned it at breakfast," she explained as though the incident were indeed newsworthy. Experts describe this phenomenon as a form of "irony." "A 'nothing' occurrence will be written about with all the unbiased objectivity and seriousness of a major event," notes Dr. David Jeschke, a legitimate-sounding person who in fact doesn't exist, "while important news will be covered as a human interest piece or incredibly conversationally." While irony can be very effective, Jeschke notes, its overuse in some formats can become "terribly repetitious and one-note." He points to the popular online website...

Full Text »

85

SNIDE AND PREJUDICE DEPT.

Everyone will tell you they know what racism is — cross burnings, causing someone harm based solely on the color of their s... terrorizing those different from themselves. They'll tell you it involves discrimination in hiring and selling real estate, and denying op... tunities to people because of what they look like. Then these same people will be quick to tell you they've never done anything like... and they condemn anyone who does, and they're probably right. But what about those actions where nobody gets hurt — little, tee... actions that come and go in a flash — actions the individuals are probably not even aware they're committing — these are the actions that brand them…

UNCONSCIOUS RACISTS…

…Always seem to find themselves on supermarket checkout lines manned by their own kind, no matter how much longer the wait.

…Insist it's habit that makes them call Martin Luther King Boulevard by its former name.

…Walk right past stores that use rap songs in their advertising.

…Swear they eat at Denny's "for the food."

…Refer to *In Living Color* as "the show Jim Carrey was on."

ARTIST: PETER KUPER   WRITER: BUTCH D'AMBROSIO

Often forget to pick up things at the ral 7-Eleven because they're too busy staring at the clerk's "dot."

...Never wonder why there are no black people on *Friends*.

SOSA H.R. #66

McGWIRE

...Pulled for Mark McGwire over Sammy Sosa.

JOE'S Repair

...Always just assume the white guy is in charge.

GO TIGER!

...Go to the country club and hand their keys to the first minority they see.

@#E=MC²!!

TAXI

...Always have a perfectly logical reason why they didn't let the guy with the turban merge into their lane.

...See a Native American and assume he's got a piece of a casino somewhere.

THE BUSH CAMPAIGN'S TV COMMERCIAL IF HE WAS RUNNING AGAINST JESUS

Jesus of Nazareth says, "Give to him who begs from you, and do not refuse him who would borrow from you."

Jesus favors more government handouts for welfare cheats.

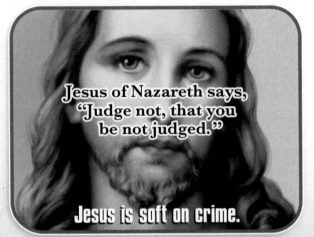

Jesus of Nazareth says, "Judge not, that you be not judged."

Jesus is soft on crime.

Jesus of Nazareth says, "Render therefore unto Caesar the things which are Caesar's."

Jesus will raise your taxes.

Jesus of Nazareth says, "Do not resist one who is evil. But if anyone strikes you on the right cheek, turn to him the other."

Can we trust Jesus to fight the War on Terror?

Jesus —
Wrong on social services.
Wrong on crime.
Wrong on defense.
Wrong for America.

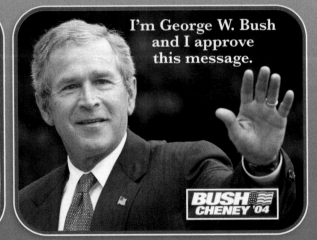

I'm George W. Bush and I approve this message.

BUSH CHENEY '04

ARTIST: SCOTT BRICHER   WRITER: DON VAUGHAN   BUSH PHOTO: AP/WIDE WORLD PHOTOS

#446 OCT '04

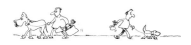

DEAN'S SCREAM

After coming in a distant third in the Iowa Caucuses, closer to the fourth-place, eyebrow-challenged Dick Gephardt than second-place pretty boy John Edwards, Democratic candidate Howard Dean concluded his "victory" rally with a freakish and disturbing yell, his now infamous, "YAAAAAAAAAAAAAARRRRHHHHHH!!!!!!!!!!! (Perhaps you saw it — the network and cable news programs repeated it about eight *billion* times.) The only scream that would have been more widely heard is the one that would have erupted around the world had this irrational lunatic actually been elected *President.*

#449 JAN '05

#449 JAN '05

DONALD TRUMP THE ART OF THE HEEL

He's an arrogant, self-important douche-bag — yet he's one of the biggest stars on television. His hotel and casino empire is facing bankruptcy — yet he's still perceived as a business guru. He's had two messy, obscenely expensive divorces — yet he's about to marry another amazingly attractive, albeit temporary, trophy wife. Yes, it's safe to say that Donald Trump has had a lucky and improbable life, so much so that he reminds us of another idiot savant with an annoying catchphrase.

He was a retard
with a stupid haircut.
But he had a knack
for making
millions. **Forrest Trump**

Parents who complain that you're not
going anywhere in life are the same ones
who'll refuse to give you a lift to the mall.

—Alfred E. Neuman

ately, Bar Mitzvahs have become big business! Families are shelling out millions of shekels for entertainment and hiring bigger and bigger stars to play the Bar Mitzvah circuit. In recent years, comedian Jackie Mason has performed at Bar Mitzvahs (go figure), but so has the rap group D12, the rock band Cake, and even the almighty 'N Sync! Which makes us wonder...

WHAT IF CHRIS ROCK PERFORMED AT

I'm so **glad** to be here at **Adam Marmelstein's Bar Mitzvah!** This is a **reverent** and **sacred** occasion! Hey, Adam, **Mazel Tov,** ya dumb cracker!

Adam, **I saw you** this morning at the **temple,** gettin' your **prayer on!** It was like **Amateur Night** at the **Apollo!** When your **voice cracked,** I thought **Sandman** was gonna **sweep your ass** off the **stage! Hey!** You're a **man** now! You're **supposed** to sound like **Barry White,** not **Barry Manilow!**

When they **told me** I was boo at a Jewish religious cerem I thought it was a **circumcis** Then I thought, **that can't be** 'cause you **old White folks** w **NEVER** let a **Black man** i a **room** with a **knife!**

I wanna thank **Rabbi Katz** for **introducing me!** Rabbis a **lot like pimps,** don't you kn they both wear fuzzy hats **hold positions of power** in t community! But the **differenc** you **won't ever** hear a **rabbi** "Man, I wish these ho's wo **just back** the **f**k** up off m At least **not** in public!

The Iraq War Mish-mosh Accomplished

For four years the Bush war mantra was to "stay the course" in Iraq. Now, with roughly 3,000 Americans dead and tens of thousands injured, the new Bush war mantra is "we won't leave short of victory." But our delusional Commander-in-Chief can't tell us what victory is and how we achieve it. So American G.I.s slog onward, like pawns in some never-ending sick game. That the War in Iraq is the dumbest thing of the year is painfully obvious. The only question remaining is whether or not it proves to be the dumbest thing of the century.

THE IRAQI QUAGMIRE CHESS SET

From the makers of THE 'NAM CHESS SET!

Now you can experience the bumbling American mission in Iraq, but without the constant hassle of having to pick hot shrapnel out of your ass. With the Quagmire Chess™ set you'll feel like you're in the middle of all the unpredictable action from the comfort of your living room! And you can do what the Pentagon *never* has: apply and implement a **strategy to win the war!** But it won't be easy! By combining the rules of traditional chess with the anarchy of the Sunni Triangle, Quagmire Chess™ replicates "Bush's Blunder" with amazing (and frustrating!) accuracy.

The Battlefield

Unlike conventional chess boards, the Quagmire Chess™ board is actually shaped like Iraq, giving a nearly **insurmountable advantage** to the Iraqi player who is familiar with the "terrain." Further hindering the American side is that conventional chess strategies **don't work** in this game. In fact, most American players will soon realize that the game *itself* makes no sense.

HAND-CRAFTED QUALITY!

The Fighters

Quagmire Chess™ pits a undermanned battalion of exhausted, homesick Americans, some on their third or fourth tour of duty, against a ragtag army of furious Sunni militants and rabid foreign jihadists. (Fun!) Play the Iraqi side and you're a "winner" as long as the fight rages on. In fact, a mere stalemate is a **major victory!** Play the American side, however, and "winning" — since it's **not clearly defined** in the rules — is *impossible*. It's a debilitating battle with no clear objective or end in sight. That's why it's called **Quagmire Chess™**!

PENTAGON
(AMERICAN ROOK)

HILARY CLINTON
(AMERICAN KNIGHT)

DONALD RUMSFELD
(AMERICAN BISHOP)

CONDOLEEZZA RICE
(AMERICAN QUEEN)

GEORGE W. BUSH
(AMERICAN KING)

DICK CHENEY
(AMERICAN BISHOP)

JOSEPH LIEBER...
(AMERICAN KN...

LIMITED EDITION!

SADDAM'S PALACE
(IRAQI ROOK)

MUQTADA AL-SADR
(IRAQI KNIGHT)

QUSAY HUSSEIN
(IRAQI BISHOP)

ABU-MUSAB AL-ZARQAWI
(IRAQI QUEEN)

SADDAM HUSSEIN
(IRAQI KING)

UDAY HUSSEIN
(IRAQI BISHOP)

MOSQUE
(IRAQI ROOK)

ABU HAMZA AL-MASRI
(IRAQI KNIGHT)

SUICIDE BOMBER
(IRAQI PAWN)

NATIONAL GUARDSMAN
(AMERICAN PAWN)

CAPITOL
(AMERICAN ROOK)

The Rules

U.S. troops must fan out from the relative safety of Baghdad's "Green Zone" into a vast, unconquerable desert that's teeming with insurgents hell-bent on forcing the American military completely off the board. Just like in the real war, this is **no fair fight!** Should an American capture a suicide bomber before he strikes, he'll be replaced by two more desperate fanatics ready to blow themselves and everyone around them to smithereens. "Staying the course" has never felt so counter-productive!

OUR GUARANTEE

With Quagmire Chess™ "the violent last throes" will go on forever. And pretty soon the American player will throw up his hands in disgust and realize that he probably shouldn't have played in the first place!

THE IRAQI QUAGMIRE CHESS SET

Yes, I want to invest my money, time and energy in a quagmire! Send me the limited edition, hand-crafted Quagmire Chess™ set! I understand that the game will go on far longer than I want it to and that I'll soon come to believe that the price I've paid is too high.

Name _____ Address _____

City _____ State _____ Zip _____

SS # (for government spying purposes only) _____

WRITER: JACOB LAMBERT   SCULPTOR: HERMANN MEJIA
PHOTOGRAPHER: IRVING SCHILD

LETTING THE CAT OUT OF THE FLAG DEPT.

One Fine Morning In Fallujah

ARTIST: PAUL COKER   IDEA: L.P. FERRANTE

#469 AUG '06

An arrested drunk driver is someone
who got nailed for getting hammered.

—Alfred E. Neuman

THESE DAYS we hear a lot of alarming reports about overweight people. America, it seems, is a nation of fatties getting fatter all the time. But like most alarming reports from the media, you probably shouldn't believe them. The truth is, we've always been a country of overeating heifers, we just didn't have talking heads with hours of television airtime to get us all excited about them. Too bad! If we had TV back in the old West, we could have seen some pretty entertaining special reports, such as...

THE HARDSHI SUPER OF AMERICA

Square dancing wasn't so much fun, ever

You was alwa the last wag to pull into ca

The seldom-won quick-draw showdowns

Long, harsh winters left you feeling les like a person and more like a commod

WRITER AND ARTIST: TERESA BURNS PARKHURST

96

ACED BY THE
OBESE
WILD WEST

Even the best-made chaps were never slimming

awn Lefty, in—Let's go!

u were ver, ever ked for e posse

ERRGH-uH-HOW-ERG-DEE PODNNERS!

DANCING GIRLS

matter that ey swung wide, loon doors were constant struggle

Support groups were hard to come by

...and so Paw was always so emotionally unavailable, I'd jest tarn ta the stews 'an bisquits — I LOVE bisquits, 'an...

Being the only one to survive an Indian attack was pretty embarrassing

BURNS

You can't go home again, at least that what your parents will tell you on graduation day.

DON'T MAKE US DRAFT YOU!

Everyone knows the all-volunteer armed forces isn't adequate, so why not join now, so you can at least *pretend* that it was your decision!

WAR FOR NOW.
DEATH FOR LATER.

U.S.ARMY
A MAD AD PARODY

WRITER: JACOB LAMBERT

#476 APR '07

#500 JUN '09

THE JIGGLE'S UP DEPT.

More than just evolutionary dead ends, men's breasts have developed a wide range of diversity.

THE MAD GUIDE TO MAN BOOBS

WRITER: RYAN PAGELOW   ARTIST: DREW FRIEDMAN

A MAD Factoid... This is the first time MAD Factoids are being printed in the margins of the magazine

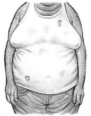

Sidewinders

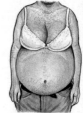

Old Man Droopers

D-Cuppers

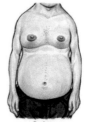

Perkies

Lopsiders

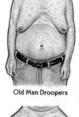

Woolly Mammaries

Back Boobs

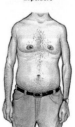

Cross-Eyes

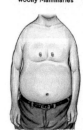

Frightened Freckles

56

glee blows

#505 OCT '10

Once you've learned to ride a bike, you'll never forget – too bad the same's not true about the combination lock you chain it up with.

—Alfred E. Neuman

WATCH ITS POPULARITY GROW! INEXPLICABLY! YOU CAN'T MAKE IT STOP!

ChiaBieberPet

VAGUELY ANDROGYNOUS PLANTER

**VAGUELY
ANDROGYNOUS
PLANTER**

*EASY TO DO...
DISTURBING TO SEE!*

Contains:
- Pretty, pretty head
- Bieber seed packet
- Instruction sheet (feat. Ludacris)

Look for it in the
**AS SEEN
ON TV**
section of your local drugstore,
crammed into a dump basket
beneath those hideous
Pillow Pets

EASY TO GROW – HERE'S HOW

A. Soak clay Bieber Pet in water overnight to ensure even moistening. *Note: Throwing a nearly-full water bottle at it voids warranty.*

B. Mash water-soaked Bieber seeds liberally over Bieber Pet in unnatural helmet-shaped design. Remember, you are making an unnatural helmet-shaped design.

C. Fill Bieber Pet with water. Moist seeds should sprout in 3-5 days; swoosh will reach critical mass in 7-10 days.

D. Relive past week-and-a-half by going to see inspiring Bieber Pet 3-D documentary chronicling against-all-odds rise to the top of your windowsill.

Also Available...
**Chia
Trump**
*Twice the Seeds,
Half the Hair!*™

WRITER: SCOTT MAIKO   SCULPTOR: LIZ LOMAX   ARTIST: TIM SHAMEY

I still can't believe it! I have a **job** as a **page** on **network TV**! This is all so **exciting**!

Kennel, where **you** come from, DUSK is **exciting**!

You know, **Regis Philbin** started his career as a **network page**! So did **Willard Scott** and **Chris Elliott**! Mark my words — **Kennel** will be **running** this **network** in **ten years**!

But the boy is **ditzy**! He seems to be in a perpetual fog!

Then...make it **five years**!

I was the **star** of this show and suddenly this **insane egomaniac dude** takes over!

It happens.

I don't **understand** — I'm **hot**, I'm **blonde**, I have a **great rack**! What does **he** have?

He has this thing called **charisma**!

Tell me, Lizz, will **I** ever have **charisma**?

You have about as much chance of developing **charisma** as **I** do of developing a **great rack**!

I think it's time for a "face cringe"!

Crazee, they're **waiting** for you on **stage**!

I'm **not** goin' out on **stage**! I'm **holding out**! I have a list of **demands**!

We **met** your **demands** in the **first panel**! You're **dancing** with **Hannah Montana**!

I have a **new** list! I want the **NBC peacock** to be replaced by a **falcon**! I want **Lincoln's** face **off** the **five dollar bill** and I want **Beyoncé's** face **on** it. I want all **verbs** to be **nouns**!

Uh, I may have **trouble** with the **peacock-falcon** thing!

He's having another emotional meltdown!

How **bad**?

Crazee's in **really bad shape** this time!

The **producers** called in **Britney Spears** to talk **sense** to him!

Can I **talk** to you?

Make it **quick** — I'm **busy**!

I have a **star** that's out of **control**, an **insecure actress**, a **page** from **another planet**, no **script** and a **pathetic life**! I haven't had a **second date** since it was **fun** seeing **Dick Clark** on **New Year's Eve**!

LemonPledge, I've got my **own problems**! I **Googled** myself and got only **23 hits**!

That's not so **bad**!

All of them were **posted** by **me**!

Barry Bonds, Home Run King The Sultan of Squat

With the publication this year of *Games Of Shadows*, the evidence that Barry Bonds used steroids has become so overwhelming, that he's the only person in the country with less credibility than John Mark Karr (see #18). While laughably continuing to maintain his innocence as he closes in on Hank Aaron's home run record, it's obvious to the whole world that Barry's slugging stats are inflated, though not as inflated as his obnoxiously bloated ego.

BARRY BONDS

IN AN AGE OF PHARMACEUTICALS
COMES A HERO FOR TODAY

The
UNNATURAL

WRITER: JACOB LAMBERT   ARTIST: MARK FREDRICKSON

#473 JAN '07

105

HISTORY COMES ALIVE
BY BEING SLIGHTLY LESS BORING THAN SCHOOL!

No Good!

NEW!

E COMPLETE HISTORY OF THE
WORLD

The Great American Journey
Meg Chunder   304 pages
Felicity and Abigail are leaving their home in Richmond, Virginia to explore the wild frontiers of America! Will these courageous cousins survive the long, lonely trip to California and the many obstacles they'll face along the way? Things are looking pretty good, since it's 2005 and they're flying business class on a 747!
$10.95 ~~$9.95~~

The Complete History of the World
Marshall Phlegm   48 pages
From the Big Bang to cavemen to the 1967 World Series to today, learn what happened during all 13.7 billion years! 48 exciting pages — plus stickers!
$2.95

THE GREAT AMERICAN JOURNEY

No Longer Printed with Toxic Ink!

Save Nothing!

Miranda Hudge: Freedom Fighter

Miranda Hudge: Freedom Fighter
Tiffany Flump   215 pages
Read this amazing true story about a girl just like you! Well, except that she spent her childhood freeing slaves, fighting censorship and working with the Queen — while you pretty much go straight home and eat Doritos in front of the TV!
$11.95

Sci-Fi, Fantasy, Thrillers and Who-Cares-Who-Dun-Its!

FUTURE SHOCK
WALLY BACKWASH

Cheap Materials!

uture Shock!
Vally Backwash   225 pages
n the future, everyone is born with 302 yelashes — except for Jacob! Living with only oo eyelashes, how far will he go to keep his ecret — and would anyone even care?
8.50

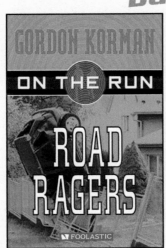

GORDON KORMAN
ON THE RUN
ROAD RAGERS
FOOLASTIC

On the Run: Road Ragers
Gordon Korman   160 pages
Aiden and May Falconer's parents are facing life in prison for a crime they didn't commit. With their parents trapped in jail with no way out, Aiden and May secretly travel the country with just one mission in mind — to have the coolest, most fun-filled roadtrip ever! It's nonstop fun from New York to San Francisco with no parents, no bedtimes, no curfews and no rules!
$4.99

Expensive!

"A Summer to... Remember?"

J.B. SPOOKINGTON

"A Summer to...Remember?"
J.B. Spookington   185 pages
Lily has amnesia and can't remember if she's the reason her hamster died 10 years ago — even worse, she's just moved to a new town and suspects that her neighbors may be vampires! Can Lily endure the Civil Rights tensions of 1964 — and her first real crush! — during a summer she won't soon forget?
$7.95

the CASTLE's Secret

ew-ish!

The Castle's Secret
R. I. P. Deadingham   207 pages
A mysterious couple is keeping Riley prisoner! Can his best friend Charlie uncover the secret of the Castle of Mirrors to save him? Yes, he can. Sorry if that ruined the ending... but you'll still buy it, right?
~~$6.59~~ **$7.50**

A Series of Uneventful Misfortunes
THE SIMILAR SEQUEL
by LEMONY SNICKET

Lemony Snicket's A Series of Uneventful Misfortunes — The Similar Sequel
Lemony Snicket   325 pages
If you love the first 12 books, you'll love this one, since it's the exact same story over and over again!
$15.89

Includes Pages and Cover!

No Refunds!

NOT QUITE READING!

Zoey 101: School Daze
112 pages
Read this hilarious new adventure, based on the hit TV show that your parents yelled at you for watching too much — which is what started them nagging you to read more to begin with!
$2.95

What Do You Expect for $2.95?

Madden 07
PainStation2 and Ecch-Box
It's got nothing to do with books, school or learning, but maybe if your parents aren't paying attention, you can check it on the order form and dupe them into paying for it! You get your game, we get the money — everybody's happy!
~~$49.95~~ **$60.50**

VERY Expensive!

Sudoku
Check out the ancient Japanese number game that's sweeping the country! 43 puzzles requiring intense concentration and problem-solving skills! It's like having extra math homework that you do just for fun!
$5.95 ~~$4.50~~

SUDOKU
OVER 40 PUZZLES!

Perfect for Nerds!

Guaranteed Highest Price!

What a Load of Craft! Learn calligraphy, knitting, pottery and more!
Wendy O'Bendy 112 pages
Now you can MAKE birthday and holiday gifts for all your friends — and you can take all the money you would have spent on them and just spend it on yourself! Like on more books! Right...?
$14.95

what a load of craft!

Learn calligraphy, knitting, pottery and more!

Hilary Duff: When the Going Gets Duff, the Duff Gets Going
Jerome McTatertot 18 pages
She's one of the hottest stars alive! But what's she really like? What was her life like before she got famous? What makes Hilary tick? These questions and many more won't be answered by this 18-page booklet of trivia you already knew and lame old photos from back when she was still on *Lizzie McGuire*! But it's glossy!
$3.25

Hangin' With Hilary Duff

When the Going Gets Duff, the Duff Gets Going!

Rejected for a Caldecott Medal!

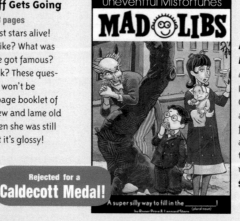

A Series of Uneventful Misfortunes
MAD LIBS

A Series of Uneventful Misfortunes MAD Libs!
48 pages
If you love the adventures of the Baudelaire Orphans, now you can write you own silly adventures. Pick the name of a new guardian for the orphans, a new alias for Count Olaf and a new town name and you're done. Come to think of it, it's not like Lemony Snicket does much more than that in each book anyway...
$1.95

A super silly way to fill in the _____!

Lam[e]

Personal Organizer and Spellchecker
Requires 7 D Batteries
Now you can organize your assignments, mark down important test dates, even check the grammar and spelling on your homework. The perfect tool to help you in your studies! At least that's what you'll tell your parents — they don't need to know that you can also play "Hangman" and 12 other cool games on it!
$12.95

NEW!

101 Jokes, Riddles and Puns That Will Leave You Baffled
Boyd Will B. Boyd 38 pages
"How many unicorns does it take to screw in a lightbulb? Eight... nine if it's a Wednesday!" "What do a flashlight and a substitute teacher have in common? They both love a *leap* year!" Plus 99 other weird jokes that make no sense! From the Creators of *101 Poorly-Translated Foreign Jokes*
$5.50 ~~$4.25~~

101 JOKES, RIDDLES AND PUNS THAT WILL LEAVE YOU BAFFLED!

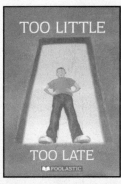

WRITER AND ARTIST: SERGIO ARAGONÉS   COLORIST: TOM LUTH

PEN AND STINK DEPT.

THE STRIP CLUB

 THE DORK SIDE

 STD TEST RESULTS

 GOING OUT OF BUSINESS SALE

KIT LIVELY & SCOTT NICKEL

 SCOOBY-DON'T!

I HOPE YOU KIDS CAN SAVE MY INN! EVERYONE HAS BEEN SCARED OFF BY THE GHOST OF EBENEZER CROWLEY!

DON'T WORRY, AUNT AGATHA! WE'LL GET TO THE BOTTOM OF THIS IN NO TIME!

 YOU SEE... OVER THE YEARS OUR GHOST HUNTING SKILLS HAVE BECOME QUITE... REFINED.

WE HAVE SPECIAL TOOLS FOR THE JOB NOW.

 BLAM!

 WIRE TWENTY GRAND TO THIS ACCOUNT.

JASON YUNGBLUTH

LIL' POPI

THE 8.3-INCH HEAD OF THE CATHOLIC CHURCH

WE NEED SOME NEW RULES AROUND HERE!!

LIL' POPI!! THAT IS NO MINOR DECISION. NO ONE HAS MADE A NEW PAPAL DOCTRINE IN DECADES!!

WELL, I'M MAKING ONE!!

gulp!

NEW CATHOLIC CHURCH OUTLAWS MOUSETRAPS

BOX BROWN

BROWN BEAR

Hello boys and girls! Look what I found! A magic Lantern!

I'm gonna rub it and ask for three wishes!

Rub Rub Rub

woop!

SMASH!

oh no! Somebody cremated the genie!!!

NOAH VAN SCIVER

IT ONLY HURTS WHEN I LAUGH

HEH.

HEY, HOW MANY POLISH GUYS DOES IT TAKE TO SCREW IN A LIGHTBULB?

ELBOW

WE TALKING A STANDARD C.F.L. BULB, OR SOMETHING MORE LIKE AN INDUSTRIAL HALOGEN OR 17000 L.M. STREET L.E.D. LIGHT LAMP?

UM... IT'S JUST A BULB. IT DOESN'T MATTER.

OF COURSE IT MATTERS! BUT, IF IT'S "JUST A BULB," IT SHOULD ONLY TAKE **ONE** PERSON, UNLESS IT'S GOT A COMPLICATED HOUSING OR THEY'RE AN IDIOT.

LISTEN, IT'S JUST A-

UNLESS YOU'RE MAKING SOME JOKE ABOUT POLAND. YOU **AREN'T**, ARE YOU?

WELL, I-

POIT!

NOBLE POLAND? POLAND WHICH IS STILL TRYING TO RE-ESTABLISH A NATIONAL IDENTITY AFTER BEING SPLIT AS SPOILS BETWEEN NAZI GERMANY AND THE SOVIET UNION?

I MEAN-

OR IS IT A DIRECT ATTACK ON ME, AND MY GREAT GREAT GRAND-FATHER WHO CAME OVER FROM POLAND?

I WAS JUST HONESTLY CURIOUS. "ONE" YOU SAY? HM. I'D'VE GUESSED "ONE" AS WELL. THANK YOU.

OH WAIT. I FORGOT, YOU'D ALSO NEED TWO GUYS TO TURN THE STEPLADDER.

CHRISTOPHER BALDWIN

#512 DEC '11

GOT YOUR NOSE

A gambler who thinks he has a "can't lose" system for winning at blackjack isn't playing with a full deck.

—Alfred E. Neuman

STOP THE SPREAD OF GERMS!
FOLLOW THESE SIMPLE RULES

IN THE WORKPLACE	*IN THE RESTROOM*
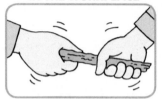	
1. Avoid bare skin-to-skin contact! Shake hands using a stick.	**1.** Avoid contact with the faucet. Wash hands wearing gloves.
	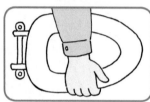
2. Don't sneeze into your hands: whenever possible, sneeze into the back pocket of a co-worker.	**2.** Toilet seats breed germs. Carry your own toilet seat with you wherever you go.
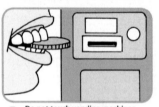	
3. Do not touch vending machines. Insert coins with your mouth.	**3.** Never flush using your hands. Push the handle with your foot. Then wash your foot thoroughly.

A MAD HEALTHY LIVING POSTER

WRITER: DICK DEBARTOLO   ARTIST: GARY HALLGREN

#503 MAY '10

#504 AUG '10

Dead Lobster
For the Sea Crude Lover In You

Surf's up on new catastrophic seafood creations!

Come Celebrate Our Gulf Coast Disaster Deals!

America's favorite greasy, discount seafood restaurant just got a little greasier, and a whole lot cheaper!
How can we bring you these irresistible entrées at such a low cost? It's all thanks to BP — Bargain Pricing!
At Dead Lobster, our seafood is so plentiful, it's literally washing up on shore! Hurry in today! It's gonna be a BLOWOUT!

New Orleans Blackened Seafood Jumble-aya!
A Creole-inspired blend of scallops, crab, sea turtle, and whatever else might be in there. Sautéed in the same oil they were dripping in when we caught them!

Only $12.99!

Battered & Bruised Shrimp
Get this home-style dish while you still can! Because, Gulf shrimp this big and non-deformed won't be around much longer. Served with garlic potatoes as thoroughly smashed as the surrounding wetlands!

Only $8.99!

Grilled Blackfin Tuna
Formerly Bluefin Tuna, this succulent dish will have you shouting "Grill, Baby, Grill!" The irresistible flavor explodes in your mouth like an oil rig that lacked any government oversight! Try pairing it with our new, refreshing Texas Tea!

Only $9.99!

Try these Signature Sides!
Plumin' Onion.........$5.99
Jalapeño Tar Balls...$2.25
Potato Leak Soup....$1.99

All entrées come with a wilted marsh grass salad covered in oil and vinegar and MORE oil!

A MAD AD PARODY
WRITER: ANDY ROSS
PHOTOGRAPHY: IRVING SCHILD

You won't find better seafood! Seriously, you won't...it's all dead.

#506 DEC '10

PLANET TAD!!!!

ABOUT ME >>**NAME: TAD** >>**FAVORITE WILSON: OWEN/LUKE/WOODROW (TIE)** >>**AGE: ONE DOZEN-ISH**

May 8, 2011

 Our family just went out to dinner. I don't think there's a more disgusting name for a food than "baby back ribs."

May 9, 2011

 So, today in geometry class, Mr. Schwartz was out sick, and we had a substitute teacher, Mrs. Graham. When she started taking attendance, Chuck and I did what we always do when we get a sub, and traded names. We do this for two reasons:

1. It always cracks us up when substitute teachers call us by the wrong names, and;

2. We figure it's good practice trying to remember not to answer when your own name is called, and to answer to someone else's name instead, in case we ever become undercover agents like James Bond or the guy from Burn Notice.

(I can never remember the guy from Burn Notice's name. I just think of him as being named Burn Notice. As in, "This week, Burn Notice went undercover as an arms dealer.")

As it turned out, Mrs. Graham wound up calling me "Chuck" a lot today, because she didn't know how to work the overhead projector, so I wound up helping her with it. In fact, I felt kind of bad by the end of class, because as I was leaving, she said, "You know, it's hard being a substitute teacher, but everyone at this school seems really nice. Thanks for all your help, Chuck."

May 10, 2011

 Bad news. My friend Chuck was out sick today. Which wouldn't be a problem, except that Mr. Schwartz is also out sick, which means that Mrs. Graham was subbing again today. And when she was taking attendance, she said, "I remember you, Chuck," and marked Chuck as being present. And that's when I realized: If I don't say anything when she calls my name, then she'll mark me as being absent, and I'll get a detention for skipping class. But if I tell her that we switched names, then both Chuck and I will get detentions for messing with a sub. So in order to keep Chuck out of detention, I kept pretending to be him today. But he owes me one. I called him to tell him that, but his mom said that he couldn't come to the phone, because he was puking.

May 10, 2011

 I feel like, if the only kind of pencil anyone ever uses

May 11, 2011

Arrrrrgh. Chuck was out sick again today, and Mr. Schwartz still isn't back, so Mrs. Graham marked me absent from math a second time, even though I was sitting right there. I've now got two days of detention. Plus, it's getting really hard to remember to answer whenever she calls Chuck's name.

I'm thinking that, as funny as it was to hear her call Chuck "Tad" and me "Chuck" a few times on Monday, and as nice as it was to get some spy-practice in, it really wasn't worth it.

May 11, 2011

I've been playing a lot of Angry Birds lately, and here's the thing I don't understand: What's with the slingshot? Can't birds fly?

May 11, 2011

The TV show Bones would be so much cooler if it were about a skeleton who solved crimes.

May 12, 2011

Well, the bad news is, Chuck and Mr. Schwartz are both still sick, so I had to be Chuck in math class again today. And the even worse news is, I fell asleep during class, and then Doug Spivak decided it'd be funny to poke me awake with his protractor. And when I woke up, I kind of screamed out a word that you're never supposed to say in school. And even though I tried to cover for it by saying "-tzu dogs are really cute" afterward, Mrs. Graham gave me a detention.

But here's the great news: When I looked down at the detention slip, it wasn't my name that was on it. It was Chuck's.

Remember how I said Chuck owes me one? I think he just paid me back.

May 13, 2011

Today was a very, very bad day. Chuck finally made it back to school today — he was still a little feverish, but he said his mom told him he was well enough to go.

In math class, Mrs. Graham was still subbing in geometry, and when she got to Chuck's name, he said, "Here!" And she said, "Very funny, but you're not Chuck." And before I could stop him, he said, "Yes, I am!" And one thing led to another, and pretty quickly, Mrs. Graham figured out the whole name-swapping thing. So we both got double detentions for the next month.

This sort of thing never happens to Burn Notice.

WRITER: TIM CARVELL   ARTIST: BRIAN DURNIAK

Some people are blessed with skin as soft and smooth as the freshly driven snow. They always look good in photos, always have a date on Friday night, and always seem to come out on top in life. We hate these people. Then there are others, like Jeff in the purchasing department. Hoo-Boy! To call this guy Pizza Face would be an insult to pizza! Jeff could eat a vat of Proactiv and it wouldn't do any good. What about your skin? Have you looked in the mirror lately? Are you like Jeff?

ARE YOU A CANDIDATE FOR THE ZIT HALL OF FAME?

WRITER AND ARTIST: TOM CHENEY
COLORIST: CARL PETERSON

PUH-FWETCH!

Has popping one of your pimples frequently resulted in a severe case of whiplash?

GOOD-BYE, SIZE FIFTEEN, HELLOOOOO SIZE *SEVEN!*

Are you able to drastically reduce your body weight with just one pimple popping session?

Has the ineffectiveness of acne medication forced you to switch to power tools instead?

Have you ever used your complexion as a means of self defense?

Does your skin condition interfere with your use of sporting equipment?

Do your blemishes sometimes erupt unexpectedly during changes in aircraft cabin pressure?

COVERING FOR A PEDOPHILE WE ARE PENN STATE!

There's nothing more repugnant than the molesting of 10-year-old boys. But what comes close is doing nothing to *stop* the molesting of 10-year-old boys when you have the chance. (If you don't believe us, ask the Pope.) Just as a fish rots from the head, a college football program rots from the head coach. Penn State's Joe Paterno, his assistants and even the college president could have stopped alleged pedophile Jerry Sandusky at the line of scrimmage. Instead, by looking the other way, they allowed him to repeatedly abuse minors. It is said that evil triumphs when good men do nothing. Touchdown evil.

While Jerry Sandusky was molesting kids, they all turned…

THE BLIND EYE

Penn State
President
GRAHAM
SPANIER

Athletic
Director
TIM
CURLEY

Sr. VP, Finance
and Business
GARY
SCHULTZ

Assistant
Coach
MIKE
McQUEARY

"Legendary"
Head Coach
JOE
PATERNO

WHAT'S THE ONLY THING UNAVAILABLE ON THE INTERNET?

HERE WE GO WITH ANOTHER RIDICULOUS
MAD FOLD-IN

As the Internet's profile has grown over the years, there's almost nothing that you can't find there! It can pretty much predict what you'll want — and it seems like the Web now knows you better than you know yourself! Sadly, no matter how hard you try, though, there's still one thing that you just can't get online. To find out what this elusive thing is, fold page in as shown.

FOLD PAGE OVER LIKE THIS!

FOLD PAGE OVER LEFT   B FOLD BACK SO THAT "A" MEETS "B"

WRITER AND ARTIST: AL JAFFEE

#515 JUN '12

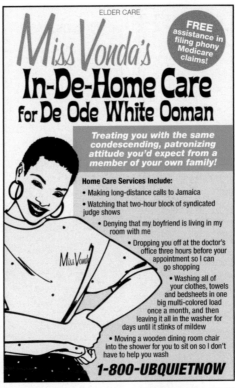

CNN.con – Breaking News, U.S., World, Weather, Entertainment & Video News

http://www.cnn.con

Search

SEARCH

Hi Guest! Sign up so we can harvest your personal information!

Log In

CNN.con

| Home | Video | NewsThrob | U.S. | World | Politics | Infotainment | Croquet | Muffins | Pom-Pom Socks | Gin | Tent Pegs | Diverticulosis |

Pope agrees to perform at NJ teen's prom

Texas DA seeks death penalty for boy caught pushing all the buttons in an elevator

LATEST NEWS

- Leon Panetta to open chain of sandwich shops
- Amazing footage: Giant squid nurses baby rabbit
- Child, 5, pokes dog doo with stick as Dad talks with neighbor
- Westboro Baptist Church, PETA protest each other
- Kofi Annan lands lead role in Morgan Freeman biopic
- Mother of gunman: "I always knew that brat would do something like this"

TRAGEDY

- Titanic centennial behind them, fans of shipwreck tragedies look toward Lusitania anniversary in 2015

97-year-old man proposes to hamster

Farmer grows Jay Leno look-alike eggplant

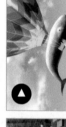

Neutered dog reunited with testicles

Quick vote

Should McDonald's be required to serve breakfast if you get there and it's like two minutes past the deadline and you thought they stopped serving breakfast at eleven like they do on weekends, and not at ten-thirty? And besides, you would have gotten there on time but you were stuck behind some old lady all the way there?

○ Yes   ○ No

Only if you just want hash browns?   ○ Yes   ○ No

VOTE   or view results

CNN.con Games: Play Now! »